THE HEIDELBERG SCIENCE LIBRARY | Volume 2

Extinct
and Vanishing
Animals

A biology of extinction and survival
by Vinzenz Ziswiler

Revised English Edition by Fred and Pille Bunnell

SPRINGER-VERLAG NEW YORK INC. | 1967

First published in 1965 | "Bedrohte und Ausgerottete Tiere"

First English edition 1967

© by Springer-Verlag Berlin · Heidelberg 1965

Library of Congress Catalog Card Number 65-25116

© by Springer-Verlag New York Inc. 1967

Library of Congress Catalog Card Number 67-25112

Printed in the United States of America

Title No. 3912

Recommended by the
WORLD WILDLIFE FUND

Foreword

In the limited scope of this book I wish to present a brief review of the progressive destruction of nature, particularly in the domain of animal life, and at the same time to illustrate some of the possibilities by which man can prevent this destruction.

As the mightiest creation of nature, man extends his influence into all of nature's provinces and inhabits all zones of the earth. Civilization and technology, ultimate consequences of his unique cerebral development, have promoted man to this position of power. An enormous population increase in recent centuries has made him one of the most numerous of all animal forms. A comparison of the alarming climb of earth's population curve (Fig. 1a) with the graphical representation of exterminated animal species (Fig. 1b) establishes a striking conformity. The steeper the human population curve climbs, the higher stretch the bars representing the number of exterminated animal species.

Many facts and figures are included in this book; factual evidence speaks louder to us of the twentieth century than do passionate appeals to sentiment. The figures make the extent of the damage

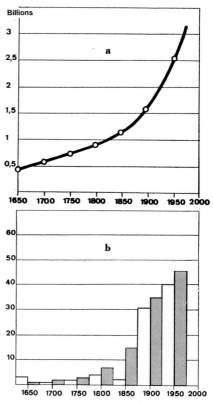

Fig. 1. (a) The increase in human population over the last three hundred years. (b) The number of exterminated mammals forms (white bars) and bird forms (black bars) eliminated over the last three hundred years. Each bar represents a 50-year period.

tangible and clearly indicate the necessity for corrective actions. All examples included in this book are presented with the same basic reasoning: when man continues to destroy nature, he saws off the very branch on which he sits since the rational protection of nature is at the same time the protection of mankind.

It follows from the theme of this book that its contents must be compiled from a great many widely differentiated sources all of which are impossible to cite. I wish to take this opportunity to offer my sincere thanks to all my colleagues and to all those who have contributed drawings. My special thanks go to the Director of the Zürich University Zoological Museum, Hans Burla, who placed his personal help and various other important resources at the disposal of this effort, and to the international nature protection organization, the *World Wildlife Fund,* whose photo-archives I was allowed to utilize.

I am deeply indebted to Pille and Fred Bunnell for their translation and revision of my book from its original German version.

VINZENZ ZISWILER

Zürich, January 1, 1965

Contents

Chapter 1

DIRECT EXTERMINATION

We speak of direct extermination when man destroys a group of animals in such numbers that it ceases to exist. Direct extermination has already claimed several dozen animal forms as its victims and threatens hundreds of others with the same fate. Causes of this type of extermination may be conveniently grouped into three basic motivations: profit, fear of animal competition, and man's latent urge to kill.

Meat and Eggs

The earliest and still the most common form of profit obtained from the animal kingdom is nourishment. From time immemorial man has procured a part of his food from the animal world and he cannot be denied this right. As long as he hunted with primitive weapons and methods, man was unable, at least on the continents, to exterminate any animal species. American buffalo (*Bison bison*) herds, still numbering over 60 million individuals in 1700, had furnished the plains Indians with the essentials of life for thousands of years (Fig. 2). With primitive weapons the Indians killed hundreds of thousands of buffalo annually without reducing the standing population. The fate of the buffalo was first changed with the advent of the white man and his more advanced weapons. A new era of buffalo hunting began with the construction of the Union Pacific Railway. Special hunting parties were established to supply the railway workers with buffalo meat. With time buffalo hunting developed from a business to a recreation and sport. Contests were held in which the competitors attempted to kill as many buffalo as possible within a particular time limit. It was in such contests that William "Buffalo Bill" Cody earned his nickname. His achievement of laying 250 of these beasts to rest in a single day will probably never be equalled. Occasionally the hides and tongues of the slaughtered animals were utilized, but the cadavers were left to rot. Buffalo hunts

1

organized by the railroad companies produced what were likely the most bloodthirsty and senseless massacres perpetrated on the North American continent. The tracks of the Union Pacific Railway unfortunately passed directly through the center of the buffalo range. As the trains passed through this area the buffalo were shot relentlessly, and the tracks gradually acquired a border of rotting carcasses. By 1890 only a few dozen buffalo remained.

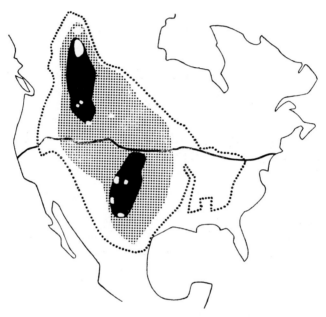

Fig. 2. The former and current distribution of the North American buffalo. The dotted line encloses the range before 1800. The stippled area represents the range about 1850; the black areas represent the range about 1875; and the white areas, the current occurrence. The Union Pacific Railway is indicated by the solid line.

Although the American buffalo was saved at the last minute through the energetic interference of a few concerned people, another American animal, the passenger pigeon (*Ectopistes migratorius*), was completely exterminated. These graceful pigeons were at one time undoubtedly among the most numerous of all bird species. The sky was darkened by vast flocks as they migrated over the North American continent (Fig. 3). Single flocks were estimated to contain more than two billion birds. The extermination of such an abundant species was considered impossible, but experience proved otherwise.

The fate of the passenger pigeon was determined largely through three of its characteristics: its savoury flesh; its migration in dense flocks; and its habit of nesting in swarms, often hundreds in a single tree. In pioneer times these migrating birds provided welcome enrichment and variety to the white settlers' menu. Later the capture of the birds became commercialized, particularly after railways made quick transportation of the meat to the population centers possible. By 1850 several thousand

Fig. 3. Passenger pigeon hunt in Louisiana. *From the "Illustrated Sporting and Dramatic News," 1875.*

people were employed solely in the catching and marketing of passenger pigeons. Every conceivable means was utilized to obtain this tasty delicacy. Special firearms, cannons, and forerunners to the machine gun were constructed. Abundant harvests were also reaped at the sleeping and nesting sites where young and old birds alike were slaughtered during night drives. Catch records from the last century illustrate the path of thoughtless killing that led to the passenger pigeon's extermination. In 1855 one New York handler alone had a daily turnover of 18,000 pigeons. In 1869, seven and a half million birds were captured at one spot. In 1879 a billion birds were captured in the state of Michigan. This exhaustive utilization led to a sudden collapse of the pigeon population. During the second half of the nineteenth century the species became rare throughout the United States. After 1860 no more large breeding colonies were found. The last nest was observed in 1894, and as the last passenger pigeon died in the Cincinnati Zoo in 1914, the task and a species were finished.

An example of animal capture conducted with a high degree of technical skill is the whaling industry. Fleets of boats outfitted with the most modern equipment ply the arctic and antarctic oceans pursuing the profitable business of hunting the whale, a raw material source of uncommon variety. The whales are often located with radar or from ship-based planes, then harpooned from special hunting ships. The whaling fleet's mothership, a veritable floating factory, undertakes the processing of the harpooned carcass. Almost the entire body of the whale can be used. The extracted whale oil alone finds a variety of uses from feeding humans, through a raw material source for the soap, leather and linoleum industries, to the production of synthetic resins. Sperm whale oil is an important basic element for the pharmaceutical and cosmetic industries. Whale meat may serve in human nutrition or be processed as food for cattle or dogs. The bones of the whale supply glue, gelatine, and various fertilizers. Several internal organs such as the liver provide valuable vitamins and hormones. With the current harvest of 60,000 to 70,000 whales per year, the future of certain whale species has become a matter of deep concern. Already at the turn of the century two whale species, the Atlantic right whale (*Eubalaena glacialis*) and the southern right whale (*Eubalaena australis*), had become quite rare. The reason: baleen, the strainer with which these whales sieve their food from the seawater, was the source of the much desired "whale bone" used in corsettes and crinolines.

For decades the International Whaling Commission has established maximum harvest quotas. Although these recommendations, established to ensure the continued existence of threatened whale species, are factually and scientifically based, they are very often disregarded by those who should be most concerned. In 1964 the commission established the maximum harvest quota for Antarctic regions at 4,000 blue whale units (1 blue whale unit = 2 fin whale or 6 sei whale units). This quota, however, was completely ignored by the nations hunting in the Antarctic. These nations—Japan, the Soviet Union, Norway, and Holland—decided to harvest 8,000 blue whale units, or twice the scientifically determined quota. If such excessive demands on the Antarctic whale population persist, it is unlikely that the destruction of the fin whale (*Balaenoptera physalus*) and the sei whale (*Balaenoptera borealis*) can be prevented. For probably the first time in history, actions ultimately leading to the extinction of a large animal species are being deliberately planned by governments.

Whales are not the only animals being utilized beyond their capacity to reproduce. The desirable flesh of several reptilian forms is sacrificing them to the same fate. In most instances, moreover, these are island-dwelling forms which never were numerous. Among such threatened species are the giant tortoises (*Testudo elephantopus* and *T. gigantea*) found on the Galapagos and Seychelles Islands respectively, and the Galapagos land iguana (*Conolophus subcristatus*) (Figs. 4, 5, and 6).

Fig. 4. Cadaver of a Galapagos giant tortoise. Often only the liver, considered a special delicacy, is utilized. To obtain the liver a hole is smashed in the animal's shell. *Photo by R. Honegger.*

Not only the flesh, but also the eggs of many animal species are edible and desired. Especially profitable collecting areas are islands such as those in the northern Atlantic where millions of seabirds appear every year to nest and raise their young. Here the egg robbers, both animal and human, find a fertile hunting ground. Often the adults and newly hatched young are collected along with the eggs. On an island near Tasmania the entire penguin population, 80 million strong, was leased from the Australian government and reduced to oil, a product which sells more readily than do penguins. Each year on the Faroe Islands, 60,000 murres or guillemots (genus *Uria*) and a quarter million puffins (*Fratercula artica*) are captured. In addition to this, the islands supply

Fig. 5. Seychelles giant tortoise. *Photo by R. Honegger.*

Fig. 6. Galapagos land iguana on Barrington Island. *Photo by R. Honegger.*

man with a further annual harvest of half a million eggs from the common murre (*Uria aalge*).

In the last century the great auk (*Alca impennis*, Fig. 7) had already met its doom through such uncontrolled harvesting activities. Largest of the Alcids and flightless like the penguins, the great auk was extinct by 1850. The form of this "penguin of the Arctic" is known to us today only through a few precious museum specimens. Other Alcids, such as the common murre, black guillemot (*Cepphus grylle*) and the puffin have disappeared completely from certain areas.

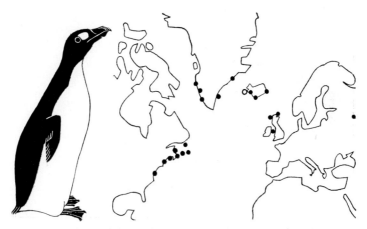

Fig. 7. The great auk and its former distribution. Black dots: former nesting grounds. White circle: death place of the last two birds in 1844. *From Naumann, 1903.*

In spite of these regrettable conditions we cannot completely condemn the egg harvesting activities. Alcid eggs and flesh provide an important and irreplaceable source of nutrition for the human inhabitants of the Arctic regions. However, the utilization of the alcid population must be pursued under scientific control to avoid an irreparable depletion and to ensure the maintenance of a stable population over the years.

Breeding grounds of the albatrosses, petrels and shearwaters are found on islands in the Pacific Ocean. Once a year members of each species gather from the world's oceans to one or more of these remote islands to breed and raise that year's young. None of these islands, however, is sufficiently remote that the birds are unaffected by egg hunters. On the Hawaiian Island of Laysan a special industry manufactures protein preparations from the eggs of various sea birds, including those of the Laysan albatross (*Diomedea immutabilis*). To aid the harvesting of millions of eggs annually a network of truck roads traverses the island (Fig. 8). Such extensive harvesting takes place regardless of the fact that the albatross lays only one egg annually. The rarest of the albatrosses, Steller's albatross (*Diomedea albatrus*), breeds on one of the Bonin Islands. Relentless persecution by egg and feather collectors has pushed this bird to the brink of extinction.

Fig. 8. Egg harvest on the Hawaiian island of Laysan. The eggs of the Laysan albatross (in foreground) are made into various protein preparations. *From Hesse-Doflein, 1910.*

Birds are not the only animals whose eggs are subject to man's utilization. In certain tropical areas turtle eggs are in great demand. The most sought-after eggs are supplied by a fish, the sturgeon (*Acipenser sturio*, Fig. 9). One pound of its caviar costs about $28.50, clearly a profitable quarry for any fisherman. The great demand for this delicacy has resulted in the sturgeon's disappearance from practically all central European waters.

Hides, Furs and Feathers

The animal kingdom supplies mankind not only with nourishment, but also with clothing and finery. Even a hundred years ago the existence of some species was endangered by the great demand for their furs. One of the most sought-after pelts was that of the sea otter (*Enhydra lutris*), an inhabitant of the northern Pacific coasts. The high prices paid for its fur and the resultant intensive pursuit almost led to the animal's extermination. In 1856 the Russian-American Company sold 118,000 sea otter pelts. In 1885 only 8,000 pelts were so disposed, and by 1910 the number had diminished to 400. When no more sea otters were captured, it was assumed that the species was extinct. Fortunately, however, a few pairs managed to survive, and thanks to

Fig. 9. Sturgeon slaughterhouse in Hamburg. *By H. Petersen.*

complete protection the sea otter population has gradually increased to the point where it can once again be harvested (Fig. 10).

The sea otter now enjoys partial protection, but not so the bearers of some other highly desired pelts. Seal pelts are currently being sought with the same industry and vigour that almost exterminated the sea otter. Formerly these pelts were a favourite material for schoolbags or sachets, and provided the cross country skiers' "sealskins"; now they are made into costly coats.

The procurement of these skins presents one of the saddest examples of the despoilment of animal populations, and unfortunately there are practically no effective measures against the exhaustive utilization. That natural populations of many seal forms are no longer large and are often confined to single islands is bad enough, but when one adds to this the facts that many seal species produce only one young every two years and that seals are particularly easy to capture, then it becomes painfully

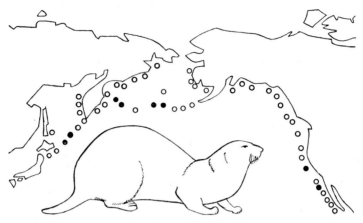

Fig. 10. The sea otter: its former (circles) and present (black dots) distribution on the coasts of the Northern Pacific. *After I. I. Barabasch-Nikiforov.*

obvious that the plight of the seal is indeed a sorry one. Resting seals are captured simply by cutting the herd off from the water. Helpless and defenseless on land, the seals can be easily beaten to death with clubs (Fig. 11).

Today several seal species teeter on the very brink of extinction. In many cases the ruthless pursuit of these animals began more than a hundred years ago. In 1792 the population of one of the fur seal races (*Arctocephalus philippi philippi*) on Juan Fernandez Island off the Chilean coast was estimated at three million animals. Between 1778 and 1805 seal hunters marketed more than three million pelts of Philippi's fur seal in Canton, then the center of the sealskin commerce. By 1807 there were 300 survivors of the slaughter, today only fifty of the seals remain. Between 1908 and 1910 Japanese hunters slaughtered almost four million fur seals on the Pribilov Islands. Other seal species have experienced a similar fate. Many forms exist today in such pitifully reduced populations that it is questionable whether or not they will be able to recover. As well as Philippi's fur seal, examples of such decimated populations presently include: the Mediterranean monk seal (*Monachus monachus*) with 1,000 to 5,000 survivors; the Pacific monk seal (*Monachus schauinslandi*) with 1,500 individuals; the Guadalupe fur seal (*Arctocephalus philippi townsendi*) with a population of 200–500; the Galapagos fur seal (*Arctocephalus australis galapagoensis*, Fig. 12) with 500 animals; and the Japanese sea lion (*Zalophus californianus japonicus*) and Caribbean monk seal (*Monachus tropicalis*), each with only a few surviving individuals.

a)

b)

Fig. 11. Seal slaughter on the Pribilov Islands. (a) The seals are beaten to death with clubs. (b) The remains of a fur seal massacre. *From "The fur seals and fur seal islands," 1898.*

Fig. 12. Galapagos fur seal. In the background is a marine iguana. *Photo by R. Honegger.*

The alarming decrease of the cheetah (*Acinonyx jubatus*, Fig. 13) and the leopard (*Panthera panthera*) in their native ranges of India and Africa clearly illustrates that seals are not the only animals for whom an attractive and sought-after pelt spells misfortune, if not doom. The Indian cheetah is currently balanced precariously on extinction's brink.

As the mammals must part with their skins, so must many bird species lose their feathers. Just a few decades ago the women of fashion wore towering sheaves of ostrich feathers in their hats (Fig. 14) and the ostrich feather boa was an integral part of evening dress. When we consider that in the single year of 1912 more than 160 tons of ostrich feathers were sold in France alone, it becomes distressingly clear how close the African ostrich (*Struthio camelus*) came to falling a victim to women's whimsy. Fortunately, shortly before this fate was realized it became possible to meet the demand through ostrich farms, and in due time, much to the sorrow of the African ostrich-breeders, the fashions changed.

Thanks to the special fickleness and instability of women's fashions, the feather trade has yet to claim a bird species as its victim. Although

Fig. 13. Resting cheetahs. *Photo by V. Ziswiler.*

Fig. 14. Ostrich-feather fashions.

this ultimate step has never been attained, it has been closely approached several times. In 1848 about 500,000 snowy egrets were slain in Venezuela. In 1909 feather merchants on Laysan Island killed 300,000 Laysan albatrosses. Quotations of 86,315 cranes and herons, 26,618 birds of paradise, and 27,650 crowned pigeons were announced by London's feather market in 1913.

Souvenirs

No less senseless than fashion's demands is the tribute exacted of some animals by the souvenir trade. This trade has recently placed the continued existence of the Pacific walrus (*Odobenus rosmarus divergens*) in question. Eskimo carved walrus tusks find a ready market among the numerous soldiers stationed in the arctic. The great demand for these carvings has caused such intensive hunting of the walrus that the population will not be able to maintain itself unless penetrating protective measures are effected.

Perhaps the most disgusting business involving articles of animal origin is that currently pursued in East Africa, center of an extensive vacation and safari industry. Lampstands, toothpicks and umbrella handles carved from elephant tusks; waste paper baskets from hollowed out elephant feet; fly swatters from the tails of gnus; and other such tasteless items are offered to an eager American and European public (Fig. 15).

Superstitious Beliefs

"An animal species is threatened with extinction whenever parts of its body are endowed with supposed curative or other benevolent powers." The validity of this rule, formulated by H. Hediger and named in honor of E. Bächler, one of the chief advocators of the ibex's reintroduction to Switzerland, has been repeatedly demonstrated. The alpine ibex (*Capra ibex*), for example, was formerly regarded as an ambulant pharmacy. Almost every part of its body was considered to have some healing virtue or other beneficial property, be it aphrodisiac, talisman, or poison detector. A particularly wide range of medicinal effects was attributed to the hair balls occasionally found in the ibex's fourth stomach compartment. These "bezoar balls" were reputed effective against fainting, melancholy, jaundice, hemorrhoids, hemorrhagic diarrhea, pestilence, cancer, and other ills. The ibex's blood was considered a cure for bladder stones; the heel bone helped combat spleen diseases; the heart yielded a strength-giving tonic; and even the droppings were

a)

b)

Fig. 15. Souvenir trade in East Africa. (a) Elephant feet as waste paper baskets. (b) Leopard and cheetah trophies. *Photo by Okapia/World Wildlife Fund.*

utilized as medicine against anemia and consumption as well as a re-
juvenating agent. The many reputed pharmaceutical properties brought
the ibex no benefit; on the contrary, its body was so highly sought after
that by the seventeenth century it was already extinct in the Swiss Alps.

A present-day counterpart to the ibex is the rhinoceros. Chinese
merchants gain huge profits by marketing the powdered rhinoceros horn
as an aphrodisiac. Furthermore, goblets carved from rhino horn are
supposedly able to detect poisoned drinks. Since their quarry possesses
such remarkable and well paid for attributes, it is not surprising that
existing protective legislation has been unable to deter the rhinoceros
poachers. Currently, the three Asiatic species are most threatened (Fig.
16). In 1964 the total Java rhinoceros population (*Rhinoceros sondaicus*)

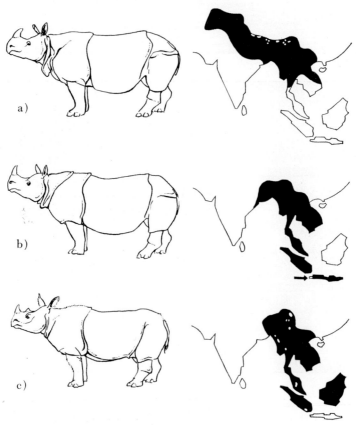

Fig. 16. The Asiatic rhinoceros species with their former (black) and
present (white spots) distribution. (a) Indian rhinoceros; (b) Java
rhinoceros; (c) Sumatra rhinoceros. *From "Oryx," 1960.*

consisted of only two dozen survivors; the Sumatra rhino (*Didermoceros sumatrensis*) was represented by about 150 animals; and the total population of the great Indian rhino (*Rhinoceros unicornis*) was estimated at 600 animals. The Java and Sumatra rhinoceroses are probably doomed. Their only hope for survival is through evacuation to Zoos and even if this were feasible, the action would not guarantee success.

Having almost eliminated the three Asiatic species the devastating magic of the rhinoceros' horn is now making its impact on the African rhinos. Chinese and Indian merchants on the east coast of Africa offer the natives tempting prices for the horns. Thus, in spite of strict protective measures, about 1,000 rhinos annually are poached in the African wilderness (Fig. 17). The black rhino population (*Diceros*

Fig. 17. African police officer with rhino horns confiscated from poachers. *Photo by Okapia/World Wildlife Fund.*

bicornis, Fig. 71a) was recently estimated at about 13,000 individuals; the white rhino (*Diceros simus,* Fig. 18) is currently represented by only about 3,900 animals.

Live-Animal Trade

Irresponsible animal dealers may also endanger an animal species. In this respect those species that have already become rare, such as the

Orang-utan (*Pongo pygmaeus*, Fig. 19), are especially threatened. Today the rarest of the great anthropoid apes, the Orang-utan is confined to only a few areas in Borneo and Sumatra. The rarer an animal species becomes, however, the more it is sought after. Thus the Orang-utan is now waylaid by more animal trappers than when it was more numerous and better able to withstand hunting pressures. In the case of this ape the capture is especially devastating as the young are usually obtained by killing the mother.

Fig. 18. African white rhinos. *Photo by C. A. W. Guggisberg/World Wildlife Fund.*

Trophy Hunting and Morbid Pleasure in Killing

Perhaps the most senseless destruction of animals takes place where killing has developed into a prestigious sport, or where it occurs simply through a morbid delight in destruction (Fig. 20). Trophy hunting can be responsibly managed and a satisfying and worthwhile sport, but there are many modern examples where the hunt degenerates into unsporting wanton killing.

Irresponsible trophy hunting was one of the main reasons for the alarming decrease of the Indian lion (*Panthera leo persica*, Fig. 21) during the first decade of this century. This lion once inhabited a vast range which extended west into Turkey. With the passing of the centuries the Asiatic lion form was forced progressively further east into

Fig. 19. Young Orang-utan. *Photo by B. Harrison/World Wildlife Fund.*

India. Here the remaining population was decimated by British Colonial officers who traditionally took a lion pelt proudly back to their homeland. Today only about 280 Indian lions remain confined within the 500 square mile primeval forest of Gir in northwest India (Fig. 22). Paradoxically it is sheep, goats, and cattle that now, after the departure of the Colonial advisors, threaten the surviving lions. The Indian lion is a forest dweller as opposed to the steppe dwelling African form. The numerous goats and other domestic animals living near the Gir forest eliminate practically all new growth by eating the tender seedlings as soon as they appear (Fig. 23). As the forest disappears so does the home of the deer and wild pig, and thus the lion's main food source.

Among the most macabre and bloodthirsty hunting scenes are those perpetrated by the Arabian oil Sheiks who enjoy luxury hunts involving numerous autos or even airplanes. Already large portions of the Arabian peninsula have been rendered completely devoid of wild game. This feudal type of hunting exterminated its first victim, the Arabian race of the African ostrich (*Struthio camelus syriacus*), only a few years ago. Today the most threatened species is the Arabian oryx (*Oryx leucoryx,* Fig. 24) of which no more than 200 remain.

Uncontrolled hunting was also largely responsible for the recent

Fig. 20. Big-game hunter with his trophies. *From "Derniers refuges," IUCN, 1956.*

Fig. 21. An Indian lion at dinner. *Photo by E. P. Gee/World Wildlife Fund.*

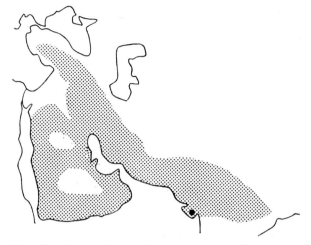

Fig. 22. Former (stippled) and present (black spot) distribution of the Indian lion. *After "Oryx," 1960.*

Fig. 23. Domestic animals destroy the remaining forest in north-western India. *Photo by E. P. Gee/World Wildlife Fund.*

decline in the Canadian caribou (*Rangifer tarandus*) population. About ten years ago the number of caribou being killed exceeded the number being born. Had this situation been allowed to continue, the caribou population would ultimately have been destroyed. In 1948 the Canadian caribou herds were estimated to contain 680,000 animals; in 1964 only about 200,000 remained to be counted. Fortunately, the pattern of life

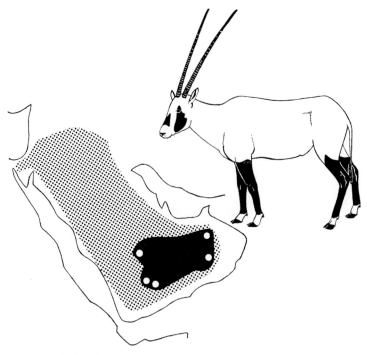

Fig. 24. The Arabian oryx; its former (stippled) and present (black) distribution. The white circles mark the locations of the last large massacres. *After "Oryx," 1960.*

in northern Canada has changed, and human utilization of the caribou population has dropped from 100,000 in 1950 to the present figure of about 20,000 animals annually. Now the tundra caribou population is again increasing and recent estimates have placed its numbers at 300,000.

Animals as Competitors

Man has frequently persecuted and exterminated animals that he considered to be his rivals. During the last century such fear of competition was directly responsible for the extermination of several South African big game species by the Boers (Fig. 25).

As they settled in South Africa, the Boer farmers came to regard the existing ungulate herds as troublesome competitors to their cattle and systematically set out to destroy them. About 1800 an antelope species, the blue buck (*Hippotragus leucophaeus*), was exterminated; in 1878 the last of the quagga (*Equus quagga*), a once common zebra species, was destroyed. Another zebra form, the Burchell's zebra (*Equus burchelli burchelli*), was completely eliminated by 1920. Three further ungulates, the Cape mountain zebra (*Equus zebra zebra*), the bontebok (*Damaliscus dorcas dorcas*), and the white-tailed gnu (*Connochaetes gnu*) exist today only in the sanctity of reservations. Possibly an indirect victim of this methodical destruction of the ungulates was the southernmost form of the lion, the Cape lion (*Panthera leo melanochaitus*), which drew its last breath about 1865.

In the United States, a medium-sized, yellow-green parrot, the Carolina parakeet (*Conuropsis carolinensis*), had the misfortune to incur man's animosity. As man encroached on the parrot's original habitat, the cypress swamps of the southeastern United States and converted these to fruit plantations, the parrot reciprocated the action and became guilty of encroaching on the fruit. Faced with such impudence, the fruit growers declared war on the parrot and within a few years of efficient

Fig. 25. South African ungulates. Above left: blue buck; above right: bontebok; middle: white-tailed gnu; below left: quagga; below right: Burchell's zebra.

battle had eliminated the species. In September 1914 the last of the Carolina parakeets died in Cincinnati Zoo.

Although the Tasmanian "wolf" (*Thylacinus cynocephalus,* Fig. 26) had a wolf-like appearance and led the life of a carnivore, it was actually a marsupial like the kangaroo. Suspecting it of thievery, the Tasmanian farmers persecuted it with poison, buckshot, and such vigour that none have been seen for decades, and we must assume that the world's only carnivorous marsupial was sentenced to death as a chicken thief.

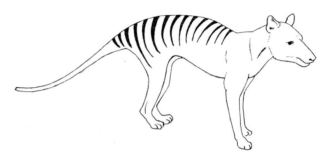

Fig. 26. The Tasmanian wolf.

Animals are also persecuted when man accredits to them the role of a dangerous disease carrier. In Southern Rhodesia it was assumed that the wild-living ungulates were important secondary hosts of the organisms causing sleeping sickness and Nagana disease. It was therefore decided that to protect man and his domestic animals, areas completely free of wild ungulates should be created. In the framework of this decision almost half a million zebras, antelopes, and gazelles were destroyed. With the discovery that small mammals and birds also acted as hosts for the diseases, this mass murder was proven completely useless.

The prevention of direct threats to an animal population by mankind's activities seems to be the simplest and most obvious task in preserving animal species as no lengthy fundamental research need be employed to clarify the cause and effects of the menace. Intelligent protective regulations, effective measures to enforce these regulations, and above all adequate explanation of these measures to the people and their governments will enable us to prevent the direct extermination of further animal species by man. Such measures do not mean the denial of man's natural right to an intelligent utilization of the earth's animal resources; rather, that the utilization should not endanger the resource. That such utilization is possible and has already been successfully achieved in some areas will be illustrated in a later chapter.

Chapter 2

INDIRECT EXTERMINATION

We speak of indirect extermination when an animal species dies out due to alterations in its natural environment either directly or indirectly through man's influences. Such indirect extermination is usually even more disastrous than direct because the alteration of a habitat, once initiated, is not only almost impossible to rectify, but also affects not just a single species but the entire fauna of the region. Ultimately the effects of such careless interference with the balance of nature adversely affect man himself.

Destruction of the Natural Vegetation

The ever increasing devastation of the natural vegetative cover, above all the clearing of forests, is an important example of trespass on nature's harmony. One of the most impressive and economically devastating examples comes from the United States. Only a few years ago endless seas of wheat and fields of corn covered the American midwest, while in the east giant cotton plantations blanketed the landscape. Today more than 380,000 square miles of once good agricultural land have become steppe-like or barren rock, and more than 50,000 cotton plantations have been surrendered to the relentless wind and water that carried the life-giving humus away.

About 450 years ago, before the white man claimed the land as his, the moist eastern portion of the United States was covered with dense forests extending westwards over 650,000 square miles to the edges of the great plains. With the advent of white settlers this landscape was rapidly changed. In the 17th and 18th centuries the pioneers diligently cleared most of the eastern forest area until only 29,000 square miles remained. The broad plains of the midwest became fields of crops, and those areas that remained unploughed were beset with huge herds of cattle.

As the soil became gradually depleted by more intensive use, man searched for a cheap fertilizer and thought of ashes. The resulting grass fires saw the end of the remaining natural vegetation. As their contribution to the natural landscape's ravishment, the cattle grazed the grass covered hills bald. Without the protecting plant cover the soil dried out and wind and water began their merciless work. Since 1930 many once prosperous agricultural lands of the American midwest have been afflicted by scouring sandstorms. Sucked and swirled into the air, the parched earth is transported for miles to be deposited in completely different locations. In this manner expansive areas have been impoverished and the United States has suffered enormous economic damage (Fig. 27).

Fig. 27. Map of the United States. Stippled area: former extent of the forests; black areas: regions subject to severe soil erosion. *After Bernhard and Gutersohn, 1956.*

In the east where gigantic cotton fields replaced the forests, as in the Appalachian foothills, the irreparable damage was worked by an excess rather than an insufficiency of water. Without the protection of the forest's crowns, litter, and roots, the humus layer was washed away by violent downpours until eventually only bare rock remained. Not many years later these limestone-rich rocks were already channelled and gullied by the rains. The once abundant forests and subsequent fertile cotton fields have been replaced by a bare craggy desert of rock. The soil that once clothed these hills has filled eleven reservoirs in the Carolinas alone, and made numerous rivers unnavigable.

The painful sequels of a destroyed forest are naturally not unique to North America. Although it is hard to believe, the harsh rugged slopes that now lay stark and barren in parts of Spain, southern France, Italy, Greece, and Turkey once supported a flourishing forest. The foundations for the agricultural poverty of these regions were laid in antiquity as large portions of the forest were utilized in shipbuilding and the insidious nibbling erosion by livestock was well underway.

Wherever man has thoughtlessly devastated the natural forest cover he has ultimately paid the debt himself, but in so doing has also inflicted his carelessness on specific forest animals whose living space he destroyed and who cannot so easily meet the payments (Fig. 28).

a)

Fig. 28. Examples of forest destruction and subsequent soil erosion in East Africa.
(a) Undefiled virgin forests form an integral part of the water economy and therefore influence both the local climate and soil of a region.

b)

Fig. 28. (b) The virgin forest is cleared and the earth planted with various crops. When the soil is exhausted it is abandoned to develop into unproductive secondary forests or barren steppes.

c)

d)

Fig. 28. (c) In the rainy period the cleared land is mercilessly exposed to the might of torrential downpours. (d) The last verse of an old, old song: the entire landscape has been eroded and wasted into a desert.

Madagascar was once completely covered with forest; today only one fifth of this survives undamaged by axe or fire. With the destruction of eighty per cent of their habitat the entire unusual and highly interesting fauna of the island faces extinction (Fig. 29).

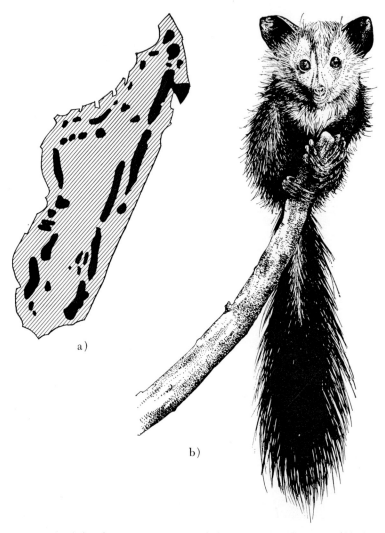

a)

b)

Fig. 29. (a) The current extent of forests on Madagascar (black areas). Formerly the entire island was completely covered by forest. (b) The aye aye (*Daubentonia madagascariensis*), rarest forest dwelling lemur of Madagascar.

Years ago the Pacific coast of Central America also enjoyed the protective blanket of forest cover. The last remains of this forest, crowded onto the Nicoya peninsula of Costa Rica, provide a spider monkey subspecies (*Ateles geoffroyi frontatus*) with its last refuge.

The great forests of the eastern United States once teemed with abundant wildlife. In these times wild turkey (*Meleagris gallopavo silvestris,* Fig. 30) and the heath hen (*Tympanuchus cupido cupido,* Fig. 46) graced the servants' tables so frequently that they complained and requested more variety in the menu. The eastern wapiti (*Cervus canadensis canadensis*) and the white tail deer (*Odocoileus virginianus*),

Fig. 30. Wild turkey. *Painting by J. J. Audubon.*

both prey of the eastern cougar (*Felis concolor cougar*), were also among the numerous forest residents. Today the eastern races of both the cougar and the wapiti as well as the previously mentioned heath hen are extinct. The wild turkey and one of the white tail deer subspecies, the Florida Key deer (*Odocoileus virginianus clavium*), are much reduced in numbers and have completely disappeared from parts of their original range. Desperate measures are currently being applied in an attempt to preserve the ivory-billed woodpecker (*Campephilus principalis,* Fig. 31). Very few sightings of this species have been

Fig. 31. Ivory-billed woodpecker. *Painting by J. J. Audubon.*

reported over the past years, and as it limits its nesting to virgin forests with large recently dead and dying trees, it is questionable whether it can be saved. How restricted particular forest habitats can become even within a large forest area is illustrated by yet another bird, the barely sparrow-sized Kirtland's warbler (*Dendroica kirtlandii*). Today about 1,000 individuals survive in a small, very specialized forest region of central Michigan.

Several countries have recognized the enormous significance of the forest in nature's economy and to the general welfare of man soon enough to effect protective legislation while the forests still existed. In other areas of the earth, however, particularly the tropics, the forests are still being systematically levelled with unrelenting vigour. To make matters worse, clearing the tropical forests has rarely proven profitable because the exposed soils are far less productive than might be expected. In many instances these soils become quickly exhausted once they are tilled. Often the tropical farmer must abandon his clearing after only a few years and fell a new area deeper in the forest. These abandoned settlements are not overgrown by true tropical forests, but by a less complex secondary forest type that naturally supports fewer animal species.

Where the soils are typically lateritic, as they are in much of the tropics, an irreversible drying and hardening process may commence, ultimately producing a "rock" incapable of supporting plant life and useful only as a building material.

In large areas of South America the cleared land is converted to coffee plantations. As the harvests decrease with progressive exhaustion of the soil, these plantations are simply deserted. The "coffee deserts," wide zones of destroyed, parched, and unproductive soils surrounding many South American cities, originated in this manner.

Chemical herbicides now provide man with a newer more effective method of destroying vegetation. Special aircraft spray huge areas with herbicides usually intended to destroy only certain unpleasant plant species, but which frequently eliminate other plants and animals as well.

Drainage of Wetlands

Swamps and marshes shelter specific plant and animal communities and in many instances play an important role as ground water regulators. Land hungry man, however, usually sees these areas only as unproductive zones or as focal points for dangerous diseases such as yellow fever and malaria.

Among the best known victims of thoughtless drainage programs has

been the whooping crane (*Grus americana,* Fig. 32), now represented by
only three dozen individuals in the wild and a few more in captivity.
Although the initial steps of its eradication were accomplished by
excessive hunting pressure on a naturally small population, man's interference with the marshy areas it requires as breeding grounds has certainly not helped its struggle for survival.

Fig. 32. The whooping crane. *Photo by World Wildlife
Fund.*

Almost exactly the same, and just as unpleasant, is the situation faced
by the Japanese crane (*Grus japonensis*). Now found only by Lake
Khanka near Vladivostok and in two minute populations on the Japanese
island of Hokkaido, this species also was first decimated by ruthless
hunting and then deprived of its breeding grounds by swamp drainage.

Expansive marshes and moor landscapes have long since disappeared
from central Europe, and the remaining small marshes, moors, pools,
and ponds are vanishing at an alarming rate (Fig. 33). Man utilizes

Fig. 33. A natural pond, one of the most threatened landscape elements in central Europe. *Photo by H. Heusser.*

such "unproductive" zones as marshes and moors by covering them with his highways or industrial works; or he drains and makes them arable. Ponds and pools serve him as convenient rubbish dumps (Fig. 34); all such holes are recognized as fitting places to discard the ever increasing ubiquitous debris which, like an index of prosperity, increases with the standard of living.

With every filled pool, and the drainage of even the smallest marsh, the landscape suffers a significant and often irreparable loss as a tiny

Fig. 34. A common scene: a pond is filled with construction debris, and a small but diverse community of plant and animal life is extinguished. *Photo by H. Heusser.*

but complete world of animal and plant life loses its home and right to live. In this respect, frogs, toads, and salamanders suffer particularly heavy losses. These amphibians are completely dependent upon water as their young must live in this element during the first stages of their life. Furthermore, they seldom spawn in rivers or large lakes, but prefer the stiller waters. Unlike some other animals they are not sufficiently adaptable to changes in their habitat to seek other waters when their ancestral breeding pond is destroyed. Although it may be drained dry or filled and made useless by man's rubbish, next spring the frogs, toads, and salamanders will still appear from the neighbouring environment and hurry towards the place where their breeding pool once was. Naturally their reproduction has come to an end. The animals themselves may survive a few more years unless by chance a new road covers their former breeding grounds, in which case thousands will be run over in their attempt to find their vanished birthplace.

Ravaged Waters

Water is one of the most important of the natural substances. Without it neither plants nor animals (including man) could exist. Wherever man pollutes the water he pays a bitter price. Poisoned drinking water; disease ridden beaches; sunken ground-water levels and accompanying drying and decreased productivity of surrounding areas; decreased fishing success for sport and commercial fishermen alike— these and many others are the consequences of polluted water. As important as they are, it is not the effects upon man, but rather those upon the water dwelling organisms which will be discussed here.

Radical alterations of the rivers' courses and the installation of dams, weirs, and other such obstructions effectively prevent the entrance of the European salmon (*Salmo salar*) into the inland waters of Europe. Unfortunately, salmon must ascend from the seas into the inland waters to spawn. Only 100 years ago in Basel, Switzerland, salmon were caught with such abundance that a law was enacted prohibiting domestic servants from serving salmon more than twice a week. Today the capture of a salmon in the upper reaches of the Rhine is a real sensation, and only infrequently are they caught in the lower Rhine. All the once important salmon canneries in Holland have perished. In western United States the plight of the Columbia River, once one of the world's great salmon rivers, repeats the tragic tale. There, too, the values of fisheries did not weigh enough to counterbalance those of cheap hydro-electric power and careless inexpensive logging and drainage methods. More than 200 million dollars have been spent on the Columbia to maintain its salmon runs, but the yield of the river has declined to only 15 per cent of its original level.

The migration of the eel (*Anguilla anguilla*) is just the opposite to that of the salmon. The eel spends most of its adult days in fresh water and only at the end of its life does it migrate downstream to spawn in the seas. Young eels complete the cycle by ascending the rivers to fresh water. Although they were once common as far inland as the Alps, today very few young eels are able to surmount the numerous obstructions man has placed along their migration route.

Worse than the mechanical obstructions, however, is the increased pollution of the water. In North America several valuable salmon runs have been severely damaged through DDT-spraying programs directed against forest insect pests. Numerous waters in central Europe and eastern North America have become stinking cesspools, endangering the existence of the plant and animal species that have inhabited them for centuries. Putrid sewage outlets, filthy garbage dumps, and ugly scrap heaps disfigure many river banks. Chemical wastes from industrial installations modify the water's salt content and affect all the water dwelling organisms. Every day the fabled Rhine pumps 27,500 tons of industrial salts into the sea. Almost daily, announcements of mass fish deaths appear in the central European newspapers. Seventy per cent of Europe's domestic sewage flows untreated into the lakes and rivers. The once glass-clear, oxygen-rich lakes that border the Alps are filthily, but effectively, fertilized by such domestic wastes. Aided by this fertilizer certain of the lower plants, for example the blue algae, multiply enormously, in time covering the diseased lakes with a thick discolored algal carpet (Fig. 35). The dead algae sink and cover the lake bottom with rotting slime. The oxygen content of the middle and deeper depths rapidly decreases, especially in the summer, thereby impeding the existence of numerous oxygen requiring organisms such as many small crustaceans and the entire salmon and trout family. The characteristic delicious fish of these lakes—the whitefish (*Coregonus*), the lake char

Fig. 35. Well-developed algae formations, a symptom of extreme pollution. *Photo by Hochbauamt Zürich.*

(*Salvellinus alpinus*), and the European lake trout (*Salmo trutta*)—are decreasing from year to year; a few pike species have disappeared completely. In certain areas the crayfish has become rare.

Oceans as well as inland waters often serve as rubbish dumps. Many ocean-going vessels are in the habit of simply spewing their used motor oil into the sea. The dumped oil spreads over the water surface in a fine film and with time finally approaches the coasts. Here seabirds may come in contact with the oil and begin the miserable process that usually ends with their death. Oil soaked feathers are water-permeable so that the unfortunate bird must reach land or sink. On land the bedraggled bird may slowly starve to death or simply become chilled and die from cold. Many birds poison themselves as they try to clean their oily feathers with their bill. Today entire coastlines are threatened by the oilpest and every year hundreds of thousands of seabirds fall victim to this form of human thoughtlessness. In 1959 when the American steamer *Armonk* dumped 360 tons of oil near the mouth of the Weser, at least 15,000 water birds including 8,000 green-winged teal and 1,000 goosanders or American mergansers lost their lives. Ten thousand bird carcasses were strewn along a strip of coast less than nine miles long.

Air Pollution

Air pollution began with the shattering volcanic explosions and untamed conflagrations of a young earth. Later man's first campfires made their contribution. But the earth and its life have always been able to survive the natural forms of air pollution, and man has always managed to exist in his own forms of pollution—at least until recently. The rapid growth of population and industry over the past 150 years has altered man's attitude of peaceful coexistence with his waste products. His campfires have grown to smelters, oil refineries and pulp and paper mills; their smoke now spews increasing amounts of mercaptans, sulfur dioxide, volatile fluorides and other acid gases into the atmosphere.

Over the last 35 years we have been forcibly reminded of our dependency upon clean air by several acute episodes of air pollution with resultant human injury and death—at Liege, Belgium in 1930, at Donora, Pennsylvania in 1948, and at London, England in the winter of 1952. Hygienists are now intensely concerned with the effects that industrial waste gases and automobile exhaust products have upon the air we breathe. Probably because the waste gases are largely confined to industrial zones and cities, it is man rather than wildlife that has suffered most. In several instances fumes from large smelters and refineries have destroyed surrounding wildlife habitats and would also have destroyed the wildlife had it not been able to emigrate. The stricken cow population in the Swiss valley of Frick clearly illustrates that animals unable to emigrate can be just as easily harmed by the noxious gases as are humans. Fluorine gas from a neighbouring aluminium industry inflicted serious illness upon the Frick valley cows.

Air pollution costs Americans about $7.5 billion annually including agricultural losses and those arising from corrosion, soiling, and other damage to materials, but *excluding* losses related to impairment of health. The effects of air pollution on human and animal health are very subtle and difficult to determine, and therefore have been too often ignored.

Radioactive Radiation

This is pollution in its most spectacular form—nearly always senseless and meaningless, and always menacing. Above a certain intensity radioactive radiation damages all organisms. Entire populations of sea-birds have become sterile as a result of atom bomb experiments in the Pacific Ocean. What huge price the underwater atomic explosions have exacted of marine life remains unknown and difficult to imagine. The various effects of these explosions on the earth's inhabitants are not yet apparent and also not yet ended. Every atomic explosion generates millions of tiny particles that remain radioactive for decades and only slowly sink to the earth. Ten years after an atomic explosion only half the radioactive particles have reached earth, hence the fallout distributes itself very gradually over the earth's surface.

Many of the particles that reach the earth are taken in by plants and animals and stored in their cells. For example, the most dangerous element, strontium 90, is used in the construction of bone. Every bird and mammal, including every human baby, born after 1961 incorporates an average of 10 times as much radioactive strontium 90 in his bones as that possessed by an individual born before 1945. The significance of atomic explosions on present and future organisms is still unknown. It is however certain that with the explosion of the first atomic bomb on July 16, 1945 in the New Mexican desert a new source of danger for all organisms was created—a danger so all encompassing that it over-shadows every other threat to life.

Animal Traffic Victims

In every densely populated land the animal environment is covered by a fine meshed net of various traffic arteries including roads, railways, and airplane landing fields. As many animals never adapt to such invasions of their environment, their losses through traffic deaths are often great.

During a twelve-month study in 1957, the Dane, Lindhard Hansen, conducted regular searches for animal traffic victims over specific road segments. By this method he arrived at the following losses to various animal groups per year and per 1,000 kilometers (620 miles) of road length:

Animal Group	Highways	Main Roads	Side Roads
Hares	3,014	2,720	600
Hedgehogs	5,377	9,345	1,103
Rats	11,557	7,198	544
Small Mammals	27,824	22,821	15,994
Birds	111,728	67,010	15,469
Amphibians	32,820	54,659	95,610

These figures probably apply equally well to other central European countries. As terribly high as the losses appear, it is unlikely that traffic alone can exterminate a species with the possible exception of the hedgehog. This primitive creature with its limited capacity to adapt may be incapable of compensating for the losses it suffers to traffic.

Domestic Animal Diseases

Diseases of domestic animals can represent a great danger for wildlife species. Populations already reduced by other means may be completely destroyed by a virulent epidemic. The outbreak of hoof-and-mouth disease in the locality of the few remaining Arabian oryx or in a European bison enclosure could mean the end of these species. In present day New Zealand several bird species including the kakapo or owl parrot (*Strigops habroptilus*), the black honey eater (*Anthornis melanura*) and the saddle back (*Philesturnus carunculatus*) are threatened by disease, particularly bird malaria.

The Indian wild ass (*Equus hemionus khur*, Fig. 36) once inhabited the expansive steppes that stretch from northwest India into Persia. Man's demands on its environment have since reduced the population to fewer than 900 individuals. Since 1960 the chief danger to the wild ass has been its susceptibility to diseases of the domestic animals, horses and donkeys, that inhabit the same area. In 1958 and 1960 epidemics

of the surra disease decimated the population. In 1961 the much feared
South African horse sickness claimed many victims. Apparently the wild
ass can be saved only by a program of effective health control measures
including the immunization of the domestic horses and donkeys in the
region.

In some instances man has deliberately introduced disease to a wild
animal population in an effort to control a particular species. In nearly
every instance such measures have ended in catastrophe. In 1952 the
French doctor, A. Delille, inoculated with myxomatosis the rabbits which

Fig. 36. The Indian wild ass. *Photo by E. P. Gee/World Wildlife
Fund.*

were making themselves unpleasantly obvious in his garden. The con-
tagious disease spread rapidly and ultimately killed almost the entire
rabbit population of France and West Germany. It has been estimated
that, although they saved his garden, Delille's measures cost the lives
of about 10 million rabbits and caused untold damage to the rabbit
breeders.

Animals as Indirect Victims of Biocides

Man combats the plants and animals that threaten his crops with a
multitude of different poisons. The fact that more than half of mankind
presently suffers from hunger elicits a certain understanding for these
mass poisoning activities. On the other hand, these actions have now
increased to such an extent that we must justify an ever increasing
number of unpleasant and unwanted side effects.

Every year about 660 million pounds of various poisons or biocides are strewn and sprayed over the earth. Most of these are not sufficiently specific to destroy only the species causing the damage, but are also lethal to many other organisms as well. Even minute doses of most common insecticides are dangerous to man. Relatively few studies on the effect herbicides have on terrestrial wildlife have been conducted though damage is known to occur where large doses of these poisons are used.

The ravages perpetrated by the spruce bud worm in the great spruce-fir stands of eastern and western North America are famous. To date no adequate substitute pesticide has been found for DDT, which, although it helps stem the still-mounting tide of bud worm damage, also has adverse effects upon fish and other wildlife. In 1956, studies on the upper Miramichi watershed in New Brunswick showed that one half pound per acre of DDT in oil killed up to 91 per cent of the young salmon. Aquatic insects were also largely eradicated; so severely that sixteen months later this important food source for the salmon was not yet completely re-established. As expected, an alarmingly reduced Atlantic salmon run was noted in 1960 when the 1956 hatch returned to spawn. Since such poisons are generally spread over large areas from airplanes, losses to the animal kingdom can be exceedingly high.

Control measures against the Dutch elm disease have had serious effects on bird life in the United States. In eastern Canadian cities and towns, scattered spraying to prevent the spread of this serious disease and to reduce losses of the majestic elm trees, is being practiced on a limited scale. DDT is often used in very high concentrations which have serious effects on desirable city and suburban bird life. Hickey and Hunt concluded that robin (*Turdus migratorius*) populations would be reduced by no less than 86 per cent within 15 days following treatment. Furthermore, subsequent migrants to these otherwise attractive areas would likewise be seriously affected for months or perhaps even years to come.

Biocides are also dangerous to the natural enemies of the animal pest being combatted. Birds of prey that eat poisoned mice and small birds that glean poisoned insects face a miserable and senseless death. The Canadian Government's program to aid the declining caribou population included a very successful wolf-poisoning campaign. Although the campaign was carefully designed, and all efforts were made to avoid harming other animals, a number of wolverines (*Gulo gulo*) also visited some of the bait stations and were poisoned. It is not even necessary that the scavenger or predator eat the poisoned flesh. If biocides have destroyed all the insects in a particular area and therefore all the food for certain birds, the effect on the birds is just as final as if they had been killed directly by the biocides.

The effects of pesticides upon wildlife, as on other organisms, are influenced by a great many factors including: natural resistance and susceptibility of the wildlife species; toxicity of the particular poison, its formulation and concentration, rate of application, carriers or type of solvent used; form of spray whether dust, emulsion or solution; frequency of application; time, place and mode of application; ecology of the area concerned, soil type, degree of organic content of the soil; size and shape of area treated; mobility, life cycles, feeding and other habits of pest organisms in treated environment; and conditions of health, stage of reproduction, and life cycle of the wildlife in the treated environment.

While much study and experimentation have been devoted to the complex effects of pesticides on wildlife, it must be made clear that biocide production is a profitable enterprise. Poisonous pesticides have been produced much faster than funds have been made available for accurate studies of even the immediate effects these pesticides have on terrestrial and aquatic wildlife, including fisheries. Very much less is known about the long-term, indirect or side effects of pesticide application. Despite comments to the contrary, there may be serious and long-lasting effects following the use of many of these modern chemicals.

Denaturalized Fauna

By denaturalized fauna we understand the introduction of exotic or non-native species into an area where they had not previously existed. These additions to the fauna may be deliberate or unintentional.

Man's most faithful companion is not the dog, but the rat. Ship rats have accompanied him to all parts of the earth including the most remote islands. Once these remarkably adaptable animals reach land they multiply rapidly, usually at considerable expense to the native fauna. Most seriously threatened are the eggs and young of ground-breeding birds, small mammals, lizards, and amphibians. The rat has industriously participated in the extermination of at least nine species of island dwelling rails, close relatives of the coot.

Escaped domestic animals are no less dangerous than rats. Wild running domestic pigs threaten the ground fauna of many tropical islands. The population of the kagu (*Rhinochetos jubatus*, Fig. 37), a flightless relative of the crane found only in New Caledonia, has been reduced to only a few individuals largely through the efforts of such introduced predators as pigs, cats, rats and dogs. Feral dogs are probably even more dangerous than pigs. Where these animals pursue their mischief, as on the Auckland Islands and Hawaii, the entire fauna may be threatened. Still worse, the most destructive of all domestic animals, is the goat. With time and their predilection for young plant shoots goats can convert a teeming forest area into a lonely steppe. The characteristic vegetation of entire landscapes and their accompanying distinctive faunas have met their doom through the untiring jaws of

Fig. 37. The buzzard-sized kagu and its range in New Caledonia (in circle).

these arch vegetation-destroyers. Certain islands, such as the Galapagos group with its remarkable fauna, Kusaie Island, and Tristan da Cuhna in the South Pacific, await this sorry fate.

The cases where man has intentionally introduced animals to a newly discovered area are practically innumerable. In almost all instances such introductions have either failed or ended in catastrophe for the native species. In 1820 the rabbit was brought to Australia. A paradise for rabbits, the land of the marsupials contained no natural rabbit enemies, and the rabbits multiplied a million times over to become the scourge of the country. To help stem the mounting tide of rabbits, man introduced foxes from Europe. The foxes, however, found it more worth their while to ambush the slow, defenseless marsupials than chase the nimble rabbits. The combined efforts of such introduced animals as foxes, cats and dogs have already completely eliminated nine Australian marsupial forms and greatly endangered the future existence of fourteen others (Fig. 38).

To combat rats and snakes, man released a number of mongoose forms on several of the West Indian islands. Within a relatively short time these weasel-like creatures had destroyed the entire ground dwelling fauna. The rat, however, on whose account man introduced the predators,

Fig. 38. A few of Australia's most threatened marsupials. Above left: Eastern native cat; above right: rabbit-bandicoot; middle right: speckled marsupial mouse; lower left: Western ringtail; lower right: banded hare-wallaby.

adapted to the new danger by developing an arboreal way of life and destroying the previously unthreatened tree nesting birds. After the mongooses had annihilated the ground dwelling life in their new home they acquired a taste for the natives' chickens.

Destroyers wear various disguises. On St. Christopher Island a small finch species was extirpated by an introduced monkey (*Cercopithecus aethiops*).

New Zealand represents the classical example of a denaturalized and redesigned fauna. These temperate islands were intensively colonized by Europeans who, over the years, introduced all conceivable animal species either for sport or idle amusement. Exotic animals added to New Zealand's fauna include: ten different deer species, llamas, zebras, gnus, Bharal sheep, chamois, ibex, Nilgau antelope, kangaroos, racoons, weasels, field hares, rabbits, hedgehogs, and numerous birds such as Canada geese, black and white swans, mallards, little owls, ring-necked pheasants, bobwhites, blue-breasted quail, California quail, Chukar or rock partridges, peacocks, guinea fowl, turkeys, rock doves, turtle doves and numerous song birds. Obviously, such a massive adulteration of the fauna had to have far-reaching consequences on the native vegetation and the original animal life. Since the colonization of New Zealand by the white man, at least two dozen bird forms have been completely destroyed and numerous others such as the goose-sized giant rail (*Notornis,* Fig. 39) survive only in minute relic populations.

Fig. 39. *Notornis,* the goose-sized giant rail of New Zealand.

Chapter 3

LOCAL EXTERMINATION

In the preceding chapter we have concerned ourselves primarily with animal forms that have been completely exterminated or whose entire populations are threatened. In many instances part of an animal population is spared and the species is destroyed only in certain areas. This we term local extermination.

Local extermination is especially characteristic of Europe. Numerous species that are still present in the neighbouring Asiatic hinterland have long since completely disappeared from Europe. This situation is easily explained geographically. As Europe is only a peninsula of the Asiatic continent, very few animal species are restricted within its bounds. Instead, the ranges of most species extend into the less densely populated Asian land mass where they often find better chances for survival.

The history of Europe's settlement and civilization closely parallels the course of local extinction for many native species. Already 300,000 years ago, during the ice ages, Europe was inhabited by man. Several animal species of the Tertiary epoch survived the early ice ages to become contemporaries of this paleolithic human. Thus, the companions of the old stone age man included sabre toothed tigers, mammoths, wooly rhinos, giant elk, cave bears, cave lions, and cave hyenas. As the glaciers withdrew, tundra and steppe regions expanded along their retreating edges and provided a habitat for the reindeer, wild horse, and ibex forms. Later the whole of Europe was blanketed by a dense primeval forest broken only by lakes and moors. This forest provided the home for many animals of present day Europe. Big game such as moose (*Alces alces*), aurochs (*Bos primigenius*, Fig. 42), European buffalo (*Bison bonasus*, Fig. 64), wild horse (*Equus caballus ferus*), brown bear (*Ursus arctos*, Fig. 40a), wolf (*Canis lupus*), and lynx (*Lynx lynx*, Fig. 40b) flourished. Two thousand years ago lions still roamed the Greek countryside. Many of these animals provided food for the new stone age or neolithic man, who finally began to settle down about 2,000 years

48

a)

b)

Fig. 40. Two of Europe's large carnivores. (a) bear, (b) lynx. *Picture from the archives of the Schweizerischer Bund für Naturschutz.*

before Christ. At this time he started to clear the forest, till the soil and domesticate as well as hunt the animals.

The civilization of Europe began in the Mediterranean region where the influence of the highly developed eastern cultures was most strongly felt. The Phoenicians established trade ports on the northern shores of the Mediterranean, and the Greeks, in their turn, developed and expanded these. Roman legions brought a new system under whose influence the present treeless, degraded characteristics of the Mediterranean landscape were initiated. Although Roman might drove wedges of civilization deep into the European hinterland, the greater part of this area north of the Alps remained virgin forest. As late as 1,000 years after Christ the entire post-glacial, large-mammal fauna remained undisturbed in these forests. The graces and benedictions of the St. Gallen monk Ekkehard IV (980–1060) mention buffalo, wild horse, aurochs, and ibex as not uncommon food sources of his time.

In the period of Medieval urbanization, agriculture spread and the forests diminished. Man was considerably aided in his destruction of the forests by his cattle, which until recently were left to browse in the woods. Keeping cattle in stalls and making a clean division between pasture and forest lands have been achievements of the 19th and 20th centuries. Worse than the cattle, however, were the sheep. Ferdinand and Isabella greatly encouraged sheep raising to increase the Spanish wool export. Today much of the huge area that was so severely degraded by these animals still remains a wasteland.

During the Medieval Age hunting was sufficiently popular that certain big game species became rare. The destruction of carnivores was regarded as an act of admirable benevolence. Whenever and wherever a wolf was sighted, the entire village was called to arms to pursue the beast with every means available (Fig. 41). Still worse was the fate of those animals whose bodies were believed endowed with various healing powers. The case of the ibex and its unenviable status as an ambulant pharmacy has already been mentioned. Another victim of this type of persecution was the beaver (*Castor fiber*). As this animal spends much of its time in the water, man hoped that its glandular secretion would provide a cure for rheumatic ailments. By the 18th century this unwarranted superstition had led to the beaver's extinction throughout most of central Europe.

With the introduction and development of firearms the danger to many species was greatly increased. In the 17th century the aurochs (Fig. 42) became extinct. Firearms and ever increasing destruction of its habitat, the once extensive forests, brought its demise. The 17th

Fig. 41. After the wicked wolf. *Engraving from the 16th century.*

Fig. 42. The end of an aurochs. *From K. Gesner's "Thierbuch," 1557.*

century also saw the last of the Waldrapps (Fig. 43), forest dwelling relatives of the crested ibis (*Geronticus eremita*). The European buffalo, mightiest of the wild cattle forms, was also eliminated in central Europe during this period. Small numbers survived in the primeval forests of Poland and Russia.

Fig. 43. Waldrapp. *From K. Gesner's "Thierbuch," 1557.*

The continuous improvement of hunting weapons, expanding industrialization, and rapid increase in human population during the 19th century adversely affected many animal populations. Bear, wolf, and lynx disappeared from central Europe; the bearded vulture (*Gypaëtus barbatus*, Fig. 44) was exterminated in the Alps; and the golden eagle (*Aquila chrysaëtos*) became a great rarity. The wild boar (*Sus scrofa*) and the red deer (*Cervus elaphus*) disappeared from many districts and in numerous regions even the roe deer (*Capreolus capreolus*) population was seriously reduced. In 1910 the last of the Pyrenean ibex (*Capra pyrenaica pyrenaica*) perished.

At the beginning of this century the European wildcat (*Felis silvestris*, Fig. 45), the European river otter (*Lutra lutra*), and the eagle owl (*Bubo bubo*), largest of the European owls, had become rare. The final

Fig. 44. Bearded vulture at its eyrie. *From F. Tschudi's "Das Thierleben der Alpenwelt," 1875.*

Fig. 45. European wildcat. *Picture from the archives of the Schweizerischer Bund für Naturschutz.*

stages of industrialization brought expansive disruption and destruction of the landscape with them. On the other hand, concern for the fate of the wildlife was increasing. A general understanding of nature and a philosophy of conservation began to develop; man had become aware of his responsibilities. Hunting laws were improved, preserves were created, and the reintroduction of locally extinct forms was energetically undertaken. The alpine ibex was successfully re-established in the northern Alps. A society undertook the preservation of the remaining European buffalo, and after the two world wars the herd increased considerably. In many countries the golden eagle and the eagle owl were protected and allowed to increase in numbers, as was the declining raven (*Corvus corvax*) population. Man attempted to reintroduce the beaver to various countries. It is still questionable whether the wildcat and river otter can be preserved as both animals require large undisturbed hunting ranges and these are very rare in central Europe.

Chapter 4

THE BIOLOGY OF EXTINCTION

"Killed off and Dying out"

For more than two billion years some form of life has inhabited our earth. When we compare the present animal forms with fossil forms from earlier ages, we can recognize the path of life's development from simple to more complex and more successful forms. This development and change in life forms we have named evolution. If we leaf back in the volumes of time it is only a few pages, about two million years, before all signs of man have disappeared; a few chapters and about 250 million years farther back and mammals and birds have also vanished from the scene; several hundred million years farther there are no vertebrates of any sort. Clearly, today's animal species were not present in the earlier epochs of earth's history, nor are the animals of these ancient times present today. When we find numerous fossils of related forms in a particular geological stratum, we conclude that the group to which these individuals and forms belonged flourished and experienced its golden age during that particular era. Thus, we conclude that the Ammonites once enjoyed their golden age, and that for about 100 million years during the Jurassic and Cretaceous periods the dinosaurs ruled the earth. Amidst the unsurpassed diversity of this reptilian group lived the largest, mightiest land animals our earth has ever seen. But even these colossals eventually relinquished not only their rule, but also their existence on earth. In a period of only a few million years the entire dinosaur group died out and left the way clear for the expansion of mammals and birds, who in their turn budded and blossomed into a golden age that has lasted until today.

From the viewpoint of the earth's history, this sudden extinction of the dinosaurs has interested and puzzled many scientists. What caused such well adapted and specialized animals to "suddenly" die out? Many theories have been proposed to clarify this phenomenon. A gradual cooling of the climate may have brought the end to these creatures which depended largely upon air temperature for their warmth. The rise and dominance of the flowering plants over the dinosaurs' usual diet of tree ferns and giant horsetails may have created insurmountable nutritional problems. Other scholars have proposed that inbreeding and the development of senility within the population led to an evolutionary dead end. One of the most astute explanations, however, makes the appearance of the mammals responsible for the dinosaurs' downfall. The dinosaurs laid eggs, and being cold-blooded creatures, almost certainly did not incubate these nor care for the young once they had hatched. It is easily conceivable that the newly emerging mammals of those times, agile rat-sized forms, energetically sought the eggs of their ponderous overlords without those giants' ever recognizing their tiny enemy as dangerous.

Even a brief contemplation of animal evolution illustrates that existing animal species have continually been replaced by newer, more successful forms and thus forced into extinction. This "dying out" is simply a part of nature's laws and is as natural and necessary as the creation of new species.

There are, however, essential, significant differences between the natural extinction of individual species and the extermination caused by man. Species dying a natural evolutionary death are almost always replaced by new forms or entire new groups of forms, which in turn bud, flourish, and blossom. When a species receives its death sentence through other than natural means, no new form appears in its place. Thus every species that is exterminated or "killed off" represents an absolute loss.

When we consider that the history of life stretches over millions and billions of years, the death of a species in the course of natural evolution was a relatively infrequent event. If we assume that even in the sudden extinction of the dinosaurs 1,000 forms disappeared during a million years this results in an average of only one extinct form for every 1,000 years. Man has done much better than undisturbed nature. Over the last 300 years his efforts have destroyed more than 200 forms of birds and mammals most of which were far from being so ill adapted that their natural evolutionary death was imminent. Today, several hundred more forms are directly threatened with extermination, and by the year 2000 man's achievements will be far more unpleasant to view. It has been calculated that a bird species which could expect an existence of 40,000 years in 1680 could expect only 16,000 in 1964. Life expectancies will be reduced still further for all members of the animal world as a result of current habitat destruction, the significance of which will not be fully realized for several decades.

The Extermination Process

The process of extermination follows a very simple rule which states: "A species becomes extinct when its mortality is continually greater than its recruitment." If a particular population loses more animals than it gains through reproduction, total extermination becomes a simple matter of time. The plight of the Pacific walrus illustrates this process very well. There are probably about 40,000 members of this subspecies alive today. To obtain the valuable ivory tusks, Eskimos equipped with modern weapons have been destroying about 10,000 walruses annually. The walrus population, however, produces only about 5,000 young per year which means that the population has been suffering a yearly deficit of at least 5,000 animals. If the pursuit of the tusks remains uncontrolled the Pacific walrus will be extinct within a very few years, and it is highly possible that this remarkable creature will be shot to the very last individual.

The extermination of such large gregarious animals as the blue buck, quagga, and Burchell's zebra probably followed such a course. Once settled in South Africa, the Boer farmers shot every animal that ran before their rifles, and it is not difficult to imagine that these species were murdered to the last individual.

Indirect extermination also provides opportunities for the total destruction of an animal population. For instance, the felling of a large forest area inhabited by a specialized animal form incapable of adapting to any other area, would destroy every member of that group. If all the forests of Madagascar are ever felled, the last of the free living, unique, lower primates of this island will disappear.

It is more difficult to imagine the course of extermination for smaller forms with extensive continental ranges, such as the Carolina parakeet or the passenger pigeon. The passenger pigeon in particular, which was still regarded as the most numerous of all bird species in 1800, provides us with a puzzling riddle. To be sure, we have already heard something of the intensive pursuit that cost millions of birds their lives every year. This loss was certainly much higher than the annual recruitment of young, and the population's rapid decline is only a logical consequence of our simple rule. It remains puzzling, however, why the passenger pigeon was unable to recover after this initial loss. We know that in 1880 several thousand passenger pigeons still survived so widely scattered over the North American continent that it was no longer profitable to hunt them, and their persecution by man was largely past. But in contrast to the sea otter which was able to rebuild a considerable population from only a few individuals, the passenger pigeon, despite discontinued pursuit by man, died out completely. The mysterious fate of the last individuals may be partially explained by the following factors.

1. The passenger pigeon lived out its last days as the great clearing of the American forests approached its end. The surviving passenger pigeons found it increasingly more difficult to find appropriate nesting sites.

2. Animals such as the passenger pigeon, which formed breeding communities often including several hundred individuals in a single tree, may require the stimulus of numerous conspecifics to complete their breeding cycle. It is conceivable that individual pairs never received sufficient stimulus to breed. This explanation is supported by the fact that individual pairs were never successfully bred in captivity.

3. It is also credible that small groups of a species which had always congregated in enormous swarms found themselves unable to establish feeding and nesting places in the face of opposition.

4. We know that every species that occurs in great numbers provides a food source for a whole series of various carnivores. As the caribou herds are accompanied by wolves, the passenger pigeon swarms provided the main nutrition source for numerous carnivores and raptorial birds. Foxes, lynx, racoons, marten, and mink stealthily annihilated the pigeons as they slept. Falcons and hawks pursued them as they flew. Cooper's hawk apparently dined almost exclusively on passenger pigeon flesh. The collapse of the pigeon population required only a few years and left a large number of natural enemies hungry and unable to find a new prey as quickly as did man. Furthermore, the necessary regulation and reduction of these carnivore and raptore populations probably proceeded slower than the pigeon population's sudden collapse. Thus, for a short while the greatly reduced numbers of passenger pigeons were still faced with practically the same number of natural enemies as before, and it is highly probable that these animal enemies finished the extermination process begun by man.

5. Finally, the remaining passenger pigeons were distributed so thinly over such a vast expanse that individual birds probably had trouble finding a mate.

The example of the passenger pigeon exemplifies a general phenomenon that applies to many species—the existence of a critical minimum population size. Once the population sinks below this level the species is sentenced to extinction regardless of further activities by man. The sole hope for the preservation of such species lies in their evacuation to captivity's sanctity. Unfortunately, however, far from all species can be successfully established and bred under artificial conditions. Figure 47 illustrates the course of the population curve for the heath hen (Fig. 46), whose journey to extinction has been studied in detail. After the heath hen population had sunk to an absolute minimum in 1907,

Fig. 46. The American heath hen. *Painting by J. J. Audubon.*

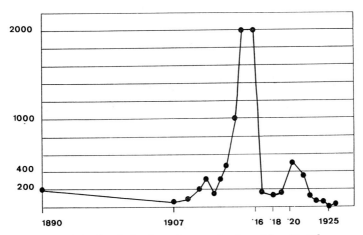

Fig. 47. The heath hen's path to extinction. *After H. Gloor.*

rigorous protective measures were implemented and resulted in a rapid increase in the population. After a short time, and in spite of these protective measures, the stand just as rapidly collapsed and in 1932 the species was extinct.

Gregarious animals such as the ungulates, seals, and whales are probably among the most susceptible to critical population levels, as the social life of these species plays such an important role in the location of feeding areas, defense against natural enemies, and raising the young. An individual musk-ox, or even two or three, cannot successfully resist the assault of a wolf pack. A large group of these animals, pressed in a tight circle with calves in the center and the heavy horned heads of the adults to the outside, presents an impregnable defense against attacking wolves. It has been observed that small groups of American pronghorn antelope panic and race about when under attack by carnivores thereby losing the safety of the herd; whereas larger groups remain unified and more or less secure.

We must acknowledge that several of the still living, but severely threatened animal forms, may have already sunk to this critical population size or even beneath it. The whooping and Manchurian cranes, Steller's albatross, the Arabian oryx, the Mesopotamian fallow deer (*Dama mesopotamica*) as well as the Javan and Sumatran rhinos are all represented by fewer than 200 individuals and it is possible that these species will not survive in spite of our current efforts to preserve them.

The Dangers of Island Life

When we regard the original distribution of now-extinct animals, we make the astonishing observation that by far the largest portion of these lived on islands. We wonder, is island life really so dangerous or are the island dwelling forms simply especially liable to be harmed by contact with civilization? Closer examination of these animals and their way of life answers the question.

Islands often conceal animals of bizarre shapes and ways. One such island is Australia. Almost everyone has seen a picture of the duck-billed platypus (*Ornithorhynchus paradoxus*, Fig. 48). Can we blame the Australian farmers who claimed the platypus was a cross between an otter and a duck, especially after they had observed it laying eggs? No less odd are the Australian marsupials, among them the well known kangaroos. A primitive skeleton, only slightly differentiated brain, and a particularly unusual postnatal development in the mother's pouch all warrant the marsupial's placement among the most primitive groups of

Fig. 48. Duck-billed platypus. *Photo by H. M. Berney/ World Wildlife Fund.*

mammals. Fossilized skeletons from early Cretaceous times (about 60 million years ago) indicate that marsupials were once distributed throughout the world. At one time Australia was joined to the continental land mass. Later this land bridge disappeared and the Australian marsupials became isolated from all other animal forms. Whereas the "higher" mammals such as rodents, carnivores, ungulates, and primates successfully expanded and displaced the marsupials on the continents, evolution on the island of Australia followed a different course. Here the higher mammals never evolved and the marsupials, unhindered and undisturbed by their competition, flourished and differentiated into a great multitude of distinctive forms (Fig. 49).

Within the primeval forests of Madagascar roam troops of nocturnal goblins of such grotesque appearance that they seem to have escaped from a scene of hell by Hieronymus Bosch. These curious creatures belong to the lower primates (*Lemurineae*), a primitive side branch of the ape family that has differentiated into a great variety of forms on

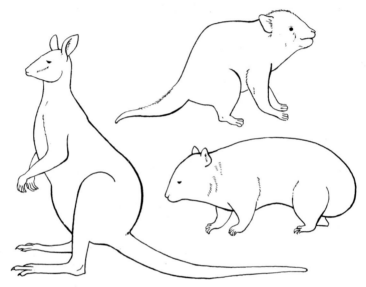

Fig. 49. Characteristic marsupials. Left: kangaroo; upper right: Tasmanian devil; lower right: wombat.

the secluded island of Madagascar (Fig. 50). The islands of Haiti and Cuba provide a home for the last of the solenodons (Fig. 51). These strange, barely rabbit-sized animals, living caricatures of Christian Morgenstern's Nasobem, are very primitive and distant relatives of our shrew.

Which zoologist's heart of the old generation did not beat just a little faster at the mention of the Tuatara, most primitive of all living reptiles? The last relatives of this "living fossil" lived in the Triassic ages about 180 million years ago. On several of the islands extending out around New Zealand these vestiges of an age long past have maintained themselves until today.

This enumeration of only a few of the numerous primitive island dwelling forms demonstrates that islands are actually favourable refuges

Fig. 50. A few of the greatly endangered lower primates of Madagascar. Left: indri; upper right: black lemur; middle right: sifaka; lower right: wooly avahi.

for ancient relic faunas. With the appearance of man the destiny of such faunal relics is gravely altered. Especially devastating are the various new animal forms man has brought with him to these islands. The now wild house-cats and foxes, that man introduced to Australia to control the earlier released rabbits, have so far eliminated several marsupial forms but not the nimble rabbit. Further species are on the verge of extinction. To "enrich" the fauna of New Zealand, man introduced weasels who complied by pursuing the primitive nocturnal Kiwi (*Apteryx*), a flightless relative of the ostrich, right into its breeding burrows. On Cuba and Haiti, mongooses with which man attempted to stem the rat plague, are finding it easier to eliminate the last of the solenodons. No less harmful for these faunal relics are man invoked alterations of their habitat. Madagascar was once completely covered with forest. Today 80 per cent of this has been removed and the unique lower primates of the area deprived of a large part of their environment. Seven species have already been exterminated.

We must face the facts. Unique and ancient forms which, thanks to long periods of isolation, have maintained their existence over millions of years are doomed to extinction within a few centuries or even decades after their first contact with man. We must ask ourselves whether we should continue deliberately destroying the last living witnesses of ages

Fig. 51. Solenodon. *Drawn by J. Kuhn.*

so long past, or whether we should do everything in our power to save them.

Not all the island-dwelling forms that have been exterminated were ancient relics. The destruction of "modern" well adapted species is not uncommon and is associated with a few, in part apparently trivial, facts of island life. Islands, in comparison to continents, provide only limited living space. Therein lies a great danger for all island dwellers. With the advent of any threat they have little opportunity to withdraw into more secure areas. Populations reduced by any means cannot be restored by animals immigrating from adjacent undisturbed areas. In accordance with the smaller living area, island-dwelling species contain fewer individuals than those inhabiting continents. Assuming that a tiger requires an average territory of 10 square kilometers, Krumbiegel calculated that 117,000 tigers could live on Sumatra, 31,000 on Java and on the small island of Bali only 560. A single epidemic could extinguish the minikin Bali tiger race. As the living space on islands is severely limited, island populations cannot expand even though other conditions may be highly favourable. There is simply no place to which the surplus animals can emigrate. Furthermore, carnivores which normally act to remove the surplus and to regulate population size are often missing from island faunas. It is thus conceivable that the strongest competition reigns between members of the same species. One means of avoiding this competition is specialization. The specializing individuals attempt to expand their way of life into new areas and utilize new food sources, thereby escaping competition from conspecifics.

The Galapagos finches, which so deeply impressed the famous Darwin, provide one of the best examples of such specialization. In the course of time, a number of distinct, specialized forms differentiated from a single small finch species that one day strayed from the mainland and came to rest on the Galapagos. One of these finches, with a fine, warbler-like bill, today feeds exclusively on insects. Others eat berries and fruits; their bills are heavy and rounded. Still another, recognizable by its thick conical bill, has become specialized for feeding on hard-shelled seeds. The most remarkable form, the woodpecker or tool-using finch (*Camarhynchus pallidus*), has specialized by learning to use tools. It carefully selects an appropriate thorn, grasps it in its bill, and adeptly pokes in the cracks of bark fishing out insects and their larvae. Such wide-spreading divergence into many special and individual forms was naturally possible only because the Galapagos finches had no competitors but their own species as they colonized the islands.

Besides the ancient forms preserved by isolation, such specialists form a second group of island dwellers. Unfortunately, specialization also brings danger. Namely, the greater the degree of specialization the more the form is dependent upon very specific living conditions. A typical example of such extreme specialization is the original teddybear, the koala (*Phascolarctos cinereus*, Fig. 52). This Australian marsupial lives only in certain eucalyptus trees and dines exclusively on their leaves. The koala is thus absolutely dependent on a single plant genus for both food and shelter, and every threat to the eucalyptus stands is likewise a threat to the koala. As the felling of all the eucalyptus forests of Australia draws ever closer, the ultimate end of the koala draws nearer.

Specialists of another type are the huias (*Heteralocha acutirostris*, Fig. 53) in New Zealand. Unique to the bird kingdom, the males and females of this species possess differently shaped bills. When searching for food each pair forms a functional unit. With his short, chisel-shaped

Fig. 52. Koala. *Photo by H. M. Berney/World Wildlife Fund.*

bill the male hammers on decaying tree trunks and exposes insect pas-
sages. The female with her long, narrow, tweezer-like bill picks out the
insects and larvae for them both to enjoy. It is obvious that such specialists can survive only under very specific environmental conditions, in
this instance old undisturbed forests with rotting wood. The clearing
of New Zealand's forests and over-zealous forest hygiene have destroyed
the huia's habitat. The last observation of *Heteralocha* was in 1907. In
all probability this truly exceptional species is now extinct.

A common characteristic of many island animals is the loss of the
capacity or desire to flee. Numerous island-dwelling birds can no longer
fly, for example the New Zealand kakapo (Fig. 54) and the New
Caledonian kagu (Fig. 37). Both are defenseless ground dwelling birds
and therefore easy prey for any introduced carnivores. Because their
island homes have never before contained natural enemies, many other
island-dwelling species are completely without flight reactions. Thus
the Galapagos buzzard (*Buteo galapagoensis*) has absolutely no fear
of man.

The cumulative total effects of the various hazards of island life are

Fig. 53. The New Zealand huia; male above and female below.
Drawn by J. Kuhn.

well illustrated by the fate of the Mascarene Islands in the Indian
Ocean. The story of the "civilization" of these islands unfortunately does
not represent a unique or even unusual fate. Before their discovery by
man there was not a single mammal among the Mascarene Islands' fauna.
Their dense forests, however, supported a very diverse bird life. In 1505
a Portuguese seafarer discovered the islands, and their destiny was rapidly
altered. The first sailors landed accompanied by their most loyal companions, the ship rats. As carnivores were lacking on the islands, the
rats multiplied enormously and soon threatened the future existence of
the original island fauna.

One of the most peculiar inhabitants of the Mascarene Islands, a
turkey sized pigeon, made its home on Mauritius. Commonly known as
the dodo, *Rhaphus cucullatus* (Fig. 55) had no fear of man. Its wings
were reduced to meaningless stumps. During the middle of the 16th
century the East Indian spice traders regularly stopped at Mauritius to

Fig. 54. The kakapo or owl parrot. *Photo by New Zealand
Wildlife Department/World Wildlife Fund.*

Fig. 55. The dodo. *From H. Strickland, 1848.*

replenish their supplies (Fig. 56). For the hungry seafarers the dodo represented a welcome enrichment to the menu. Great numbers of the "living fleshpot" were taken on board the ships and there consumed. In 1598 the island became a Dutch penal colony. Convicts released on the island brought pigs with them and a number of these ran wild. In close cooperation with the rats, the pigs set about destroying the eggs laid by the ground-nesting dodo. Twenty years later the dodo was already a zoological rarity. About 1681 the last of the species perished. All that remains of the dodo today is a foot in the British Museum, a head in

Fig. 56. The first Dutchmen arrive on Mauritius. *Contemporary representation.*

Copenhagen, a further small fragment in Prague, a few bones, and some contemporary Dutch still lifes.

But the Mascarenes' tale of woe is not ended. Among the numerous forest birds which lost their home was the white starling, *Fregilupus varius*. During the 19th century the once complete forest cover was transformed into an uninterrupted blanket of tea and sugar plantations. In 1835 the last *Fregilupus* was observed; today we have two museum specimens. Of the 45 original bird species on the Mascarenes only 21 have managed to survive. The great task of destroying 24 species was achieved entirely through the concerted efforts of man, rats, and pigs.

Biologically viewed, islands often occur on the continents. From this viewpoint, fresh water lakes often represent islands. Lake Ladoga near

Leningrad and Lake Baikal in innermost Asia are inhabited by seals that live completely isolated from their relatives on the sea coasts. Certain caves represent similar inland islands with their own distinctive life forms. One of these modern cave dwellers is the olm, *Proteus*, an eel-like amphibian of the southern European limestone caves. Other such forms lead their specialized existence in caves throughout the world. These isolated species could be quickly and completely destroyed by slight changes in the water's temperature or salt content, or by a sudden collapse of the cave itself.

Individual mountain ranges are also islands in the biological sense. As many mountain animals are confined to a specific altitudinal range, there is practically no population exchange between individual peaks. Scattered populations remain restricted to the higher elevations and do not move down across the valleys. Thus in Eurasia various mountain ranges are inhabited by different races of ibex, while different sub-species of mountain sheep are similarly separated in western North America.

In southwest China, in the province of Szechuan, lives a large bear-like relative of the racoon—the giant panda (*Ailuropoda melanoleuca*, Fig. 57). This near legendary creature feeds almost exclusively on bamboo shoots. When we compare the panda's distribution with that of west China's bamboo forests, we find that the two areas coincide exactly. The panda, so to speak, lives on a vegetational island and is exposed to the same risks as every other island dwelling animal.

Fig. 57. Giant panda. *Photo by F. Vollmar/World Wildlife Fund.*

Time and man have recast the role of islands. Before the appearance of man these areas represented especially secure regions to numerous plants and animals, and allowed the undisturbed development and diversification of a great richness of life forms; today they are among the most perilous zones of the earth. The protection of our island dwelling forms now merits and requires special attention.

The Balance of Nature

All organisms in a given environment are directly or indirectly dependent upon each other; they build a living community or biocoenosis. Each biocoenosis is further dependent upon the surrounding inanimate nature: air, soil, and water. In various ways these factors are in turn dependent upon the living organisms. With the passage of time, a natural equilibrium, outwardly stable but constantly changing and rebalancing itself, is developed between these components of nature's household. This balance we name the biological equilibrium. Some of the most elementary interrelationships within such a balanced system will be briefly mentioned (Fig. 58).

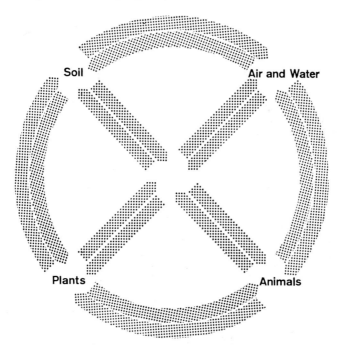

Fig. 58. The four main components of nature's household—soil; air and water; plants; animals—and their mutual dependency.

Although themselves components of inanimate or nonliving nature, *water* and certain of the *atmospheric gases* are absolutely essential to all higher forms of life. Most organisms cannot live without the atmospheric gases, and without moisture another of life's bases—soil—dries out and crumbles to useless dust. Water falling to the earth as rain or snow must be retained near the soil surface; if it flows away too quickly the living organisms wilt or thirst. Not only the soil itself, but also moss layers in the forests provide good water reservoirs.

Soil's important role in the water cycle has just been mentioned. Soil also provides the absolutely essential substratum for higher plant life and offers many animals shelter. Once dead these plants and animals may be decomposed and transformed into soil through the industry of numerous microorganisms. Plant roots help hold the soil together and protect it from being blown or washed away; earthworms homogenize it and keep it porous.

Plant cover above the soil, and plant roots within it shelter and hold the valuable humus in place. Plants are also an important link in the water cycle and help maintain a perpetual water supply. Only plants can produce living matter from inorganic substances such as nitrogen, carbon dioxide, and water. Thus without plants there could be no animal life. Plants utilize the carbon dioxide given off by animals and release the oxygen required by animals for respiration. Many plants are further dependent upon animals for their pollination and distribution of seeds.

Animals, particularly the smaller forms, help in the construction of humus. Earthworms churn the humus and mineral portions of the soil into a more fertile mixture. Insects aid in the pollination of flowering plants. Numerous animals distribute plant seeds in various ways. On the other hand, animals are dependent upon all other components of nature, especially the plants which provide their food. Every animal food chain must originate in a plant; for example: pike—perch—whitefish—small crustaceans—algae; or, vulture—stork carcass—frogs—gnats and midges—cattle blood—grass.

If man influences any one of the complexly and delicately interrelated components of this living, modulating equilibrium, a significant displacement which can lead to the destruction of an entire environment may result. We have already seen numerous examples of man's tinkering with the balance of nature in the chapter on indirect extermination. As a rule, the more fundamental the change man brings to this balanced system, the more catastrophic are the results. For example, the sinking of the ground water level may desiccate the soil and thereby destroy the entire plant and animal life of an area, ultimately creating a desert. Under certain circumstances a single encroachment on the system's periphery can produce just as grave results. Man considered it insignificant when a few goats were allowed to roam wild on the Galapagos Islands, but this act had the same far-reaching consequences as the sinking ground water mentioned above. The goats systematically eliminated the vegetation; the soil dried out; the areas became first steppe-like and then more and more like desert. The entire animal life of the islands' interior is now seriously threatened.

Grave consequences to the biological balance do not always result from interreactions **between** the fundamental components of nature's household which we have briefly discussed. As we saw in the chapter on denaturalized faunas, disarrangements that occur entirely **within** the animal component can have very unpleasant effects. For instance, when man deprives carnivores of their natural food source, they begin to prey on domestic animals. If during the critical spring period after they have emerged from their dens and before the wild fruits are ripe, the alpine and pyrenean bears find insufficient winter kill in the avalanche beds, they turn their attentions to the domestic animals.

Still more fateful are the consequences when man attempts to maintain a wild animal population free from natural carnivores. The unwelcome increase of crows and magpies in Europe is a result of the deliberate destruction of predatory birds which unfortunately is still practiced in many areas. The crows' main enemies, hawks and the eagle owl, have been exterminated throughout large areas of Europe. Without natural enemies, herbivores can build up a breeding momenum that is difficult to retard and which may increase to the point where the animals exhaust the available food supply. In parts of Europe where man exterminated the fox, rabbits have mushroomed into a genuine plague. Hunting preserves in central Europe are badly overpopulated by roe deer which cause extensive damage to the forests. In the Spol catchment of the Swiss National Park, the increase in red deer numbers has reached devastating proportions. In much of central Europe roe and red deer no longer have any natural enemies; the wolf and lynx which at one time regulated the deer populations have long since been exterminated.

Figure 59 illustrates how uncurbed increase can lead to the ultimate self-destruction of an animal population. On the Kaibab Plateau, a big game refuge in northern Arizona, all carnivores were destroyed to provide the deer with complete protection. As a consequence, the deer increased to such an extent that the browse plants were damaged almost beyond recovery. In this instance the activities of the carnivores had actually been contributing to the preservation of the deer herd.

Carnivores often play an important role in preserving the health of their prey. The fish otter, for example, helps to maintain a healthy fish

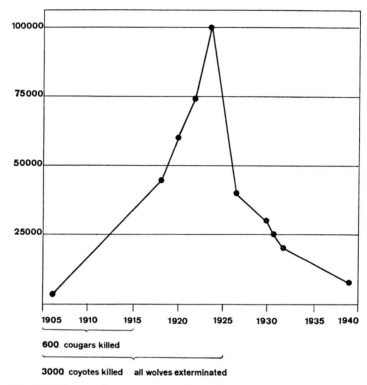

Fig. 59. The population curve of the Kaibab Plateau deer population before and after the destruction of the predators. *After H. Gloor.*

population by capturing primarily sick and weakened fish and thereby hindering a disease outbreak of epidemic proportions. Under natural conditions wolves, cougars, and other large carnivores find unhealthy animals easiest to catch and thereby help cleanse the prey population of undesirable sources of infection.

Far-reaching changes in the biological equilibrium can also result from monocultures, the cultivation of single species over vast areas, such as the South American coffee plantations, the broad expanses of sugar cane in Central America, the cotton fields of eastern United States, and the extensive single species forests that man was still fostering only a few years ago. Such monocultures support an animal world of very few species. The few forms that do inhabit monocultures, however, can increase and become such pests that man is nearly defenseless against their numbers. The pine moth which destroyed expansive areas of pure Scotch pine could not have reached such destructive proportions had the pine been mixed with other trees. In Africa, certain weaver birds of the genus *Quelea* increased at an enormous rate when grain and millet cultivation offered them an inexhaustible food supply. In swarms of millions that actually darken the skies, the birds—now ravaging pests—swoop down on the crops and destroy them.

Man and the Balance of Nature

Among all of earth's organisms man now enjoys a special position: he is no longer restricted to a particular biocoenosis. He can and does inhabit the jungles, deserts, and polar regions. The time is not far distant when he will be making space his home for extended periods. Technology gave man this power; he can divert mighty rivers, flatten entire mountains, make complete islands vanish. Aided by his agents man has become earth's most powerful force. Soon this might will assume cosmic dimensions in that man, with the help of atomic power, will be capable of such feats as changing our earth into a completely different heavenly body; for example, into a supernova.

Man no longer recognizes natural enemies with the exception of some of the disease causing organisms. The consequence of these powers has been an enormous population increase, whose course reminds us only too much of the population curve for the Kaibab Plateau deer herd.

Enormous population increase and technological power have allowed man to extend his influence into even the remotest regions of our earth. The ocean fauna of the deepest Pacific is no freer from this influence than the biocoenoses of the New Mexican desert. Even though man is no longer restricted to a specific biocoenosis and we could correctly say that the entire earth has become his home, he is still, for better or worse, dependent upon nature. Like every other organism man requires the five major components of nature's household for his existence: air, water, soil, plants, and animals. These five components, however, are meaningful only when combined. They are so subtly interdependent and mutually restricting that man will never be successful in maintaining a purely artificial balance with nothing but cultivated plants and domesticated animals; he is not capable of replacing the natural biocoenoses with a synthetic system of his own making. The continued existence of many natural biocoenoses is necessary if our earth is to be preserved and continue developing. If man attempts to refute this knowledge he will ultimately destroy himself.

Chapter 5

PROTECTING NATURE

At the beginning of this chapter we are certainly permitted to ask ourselves whether the protection of nature is actually justified, or whether it is simply the mission of a small group of eccentric nature fanatics. We can substantiate the urgency for sensible protection of nature with purely objective or technical facts as well as with subjective, idealistic arguments.

The main objective argument for the preservation of natural landscapes and biocoenoses is the dependency of man upon nature. We have discussed several examples of this dependency in the previous chapters. An example of man's direct dependency upon nature is the high seas fisheries, one of the important sources of human nutrition. Agriculture and forestry are examples of indirect dependency. Although these crops are often not entirely natural, they still depend ultimately upon healthy natural soil and water relationships.

A further argument against the extermination of specific plant and animal forms is that we know far too little about the roles most organisms play in nature's household to foresee the damage that may result from their extermination.

The recreational possibilities provided by nature constitute a further objective argument for its preservation. Opportunity to relax in nature is increasingly becoming a genuine requirement of the city dweller. Outdoor recreation is an important factor in his physical and mental well-being.

Finally, science has an obligation and a right to study all life forms that inhabit our earth. To date only a minute fraction of the total plant and animal life has been the object of organized study. For most organisms we know the name, distribution, and little more; for many not even that. With every animal or plant that disappears we lose one more possibility to penetrate and understand the diversity and the laws of life.

Among the idealistic or subjective arguments for nature's protection, our responsibility to coming generations is the most salient. We cannot assume the moral right of bequeathing our descendents a devastated world.

The aesthete feels that nature is worthy of protection because it is beautiful and harmonious, and because the destruction of nature would destroy this harmony. The moral philosopher recognizes that nature is based on universal laws, and because he feels that every disturbance of this order is wrong, he also must support the protection of nature. Also among the subjective arguments are those of the religious man who considers nature a divine creation for which he feels reverence and awe. If he acts against this recognition, he disregards the will of the Creator.

Acknowledgement of these arguments, subjective and objective, makes the protection of nature a necessity. Nature's protection, however, must never become an end in itself. As the most powerful of all nature's creations, man is obliged to stand as earth's mortal source of guidance, and not aloof—a patient, harmless critic—as many nature fanatics would have it. The protection of nature must have the preservation of mankind as its ultimate end. Man should and must utilize nature wherever he can and wants; but, this utilization must not cause permanent damage to the natural equilibrium. To fully appreciate the following chapters we must acknowledge the mutual dependencies and interrelationships that exist between man and nature.

The Necessity of Research

Can we achieve effective protection of nature at all? This is a legitimate question. For example, of what actual significance to the preservation of the species is the feeding of song birds in winter; the provision of nest boxes for starlings; or the declaration of an area as an inviolable reserve?

Man must know and understand the way of life of the organism he wishes to protect before he can effectively protect it. This is the most fundamental prerequisite of practicable protection measures. Without penetrating research it is impossible to conduct sensible protection, conservation, or management of nature. Let us assume that we wish to protect a certain species, the river otter for instance. We must first ask and answer the following questions: What does it eat? How much food is available for it? Is it territorial? How large and what type of territory or hunting ground does each individual require? Does it wander or migrate? Does it lead a solitary life, live in pairs, or perhaps even in large groups? How many otters are currently in the area to be protected? What is the distribution of existing animals in age and sex classes? What are the rates of recruitment and mortality or how fast will the population grow? Where and when are the young born? What are the otter's diseases, natural enemies, and competitors? Is the otter able to withstand man's encroachment on its environment? How heavily is it hunted? Is it pursued as a pest, for its pelt, or for any other reason? Does the otter play a role in folk superstitions or in folk medicine?

For the protection of larger animal groups or certain landscapes we require still more comprehensive knowledge. Since such large projects demand considerable expense of human and other resources they must be especially carefully planned and certainly not misdirected. That effective nature protection is impossible without a well established scientific basis, is well illustrated by the example of the Serengeti steppe. A portion of this steppe in Tanzania (formerly Tanganyika), one of the richest wildlife areas in the world, was proclaimed a game sanctuary while the area was still under British colonial government. Later it was decided to shift the park boundaries and cede the entire eastern portion except the particularly game rich Ngorongoro Crater to the Masai herdsmen, and in compensation to incorporate an area north of the park. Because the animals are intensively hunted outside the park boundaries, these legal barriers are meaningful only when they encompass the animals throughout the year. The Serengeti herds, however, complicate protective measures by performing annual migrations. English and German scientists therefore attempted to determine the extent and cause of these migrations and the numbers of animals involved. The work of Dr. B. Grzimek, Director of the Frankfurt Zoo, was especially helpful in clarifying the problem. He censused the animals, marked them and observed their migrations. The main results of his work follow.

1. The total big game population of Serengeti National Park consisted of only about 367,000 animals instead of the previously estimated 1,000,000.

2. The herds undertook periodic migrations which at times led them outside not only the former, but also the newly proposed park boundaries.

3. The main reason for these migrations was the animals' preference for specific grasses which at certain times of the year were found only outside the park boundaries.

From these results we conclude that not only does the much smaller than originally estimated game population require better supervision, but also that new borders must be established to enclose and protect the wandering herds during the entire year. This incident demonstrates a basic requirement for every nature protection project: necessary scientific knowledge must be gathered and factual foundations laid before sensible plans can be made.

Nature Protection Through Conservation

Conservation attempts to preserve existing organisms or biocoenoses. Legal regulations governing the protection of landscapes, animals, and plants constitute protective measures of the simplest nature. In the fields of hunting and fishing, protective measures of various sorts are by no means new. Man has long employed restrictive legislation to prohibit the slaying of certain animals during specific periods or to establish annual upper limits to the numbers of animals that could be killed. Unfortunately, in several European countries such regulations are often determined solely by the *Jägerschaft,* the hunting society which also controls the game preserves. We certainly do not wish to deny the hunters' good intentions or their desire to preserve the game stocks, but many of their regulations are made without regard to biological knowledge. As a result, some game animals such as roe and red deer are often excessively protected, and certain rules serve more to damage than preserve the biological equilibrium of the hunting reserves. Examples are the senseless attempts to reduce natural predation and the perhaps chivalrous though completely unbiological and nonsensical "buck law" hunting ethic which prohibits the shooting of females.

Man commonly attempts to conserve a species by placing it under complete protection. With this method he has already had considerable success in the plant world. In most European countries a great number of plants such as the lady's slipper orchid (*Cypripedium calceolus*) are completely protected. In spite of great resistance from the uninformed, a few European countries have decided to protect the golden eagle and eagle owl. The establishment of protection for all birds of prey including the owls is making headway, as is the promotion of complete protection for certain European carnivores such as the otter, marten (*Martes martes*), wild cat, and lynx. Unfortunately, this promotion must advance against hardheaded resistance from the public, as in many circles the absurd notion prevails that predators are unredeemably destructive. Even the completely false horror tales about child-stealing eagles are difficult to oppose, and when someplace in Europe an imaginative soul believes he has seen lynx tracks, the press compounds difficulties by disseminating foolish but eagerly believed commentaries usually quoted without reserve from the aged, exaggerated portrayals in Brehm's *Thierleben.* One of the most persecuted and least protected of all European animal species is the wild boar. Wherever this impressive creature suddenly appears the hunters sense the approach of their hour of greatness. They congregate in mobs, pursue, and not surprisingly, kill the beast. It makes no difference whether it is an old boar, a pregnant sow, or a half-grown youngster. The great anticipation of their picture in the local weekly— the glorious victor and his coveted booty—and the subsequent joyous celebration that culminates such a valient deed allows the hunters to conveniently forget their hallowed hunting ethics. Naturally, we are not allowed to forget that wild boars are capable of causing considerable damage in fields and pastures. The responsibility for the damage which the farmers and foresters accrue must of course be borne by the legislative body which has placed the animal under protection. This damage, however, is of an order of magnitude which almost completely vanishes among the other expenses of a modern state. Furthermore, it is highly unlikely that the wild boar causes more extensive damage than the over-protected, over-populated roe and red deer stands. North American hunters cannot ridicule the fate of the wild boar and the apparent simple-mindedness of their European cousins. In many parts of the new world, counterparts of the European wild boar such as the wolf and puma or cougar suffer the same fate.

Government protective regulations are meaningful only when resources for their effective execution are provided. To this end, a sufficient number of game wardens are necessary, and hunters must be well acquainted with the laws they are to abide by and the species they wish to shoot. In many places the latter requirement for effective regulation has been met by the establishment of hunting examinations. Tropical areas provide the greatest difficulties in enforcing protective legislation. The native tribesmen, often illiterate, concern themselves very little with official decrees and ordinances, and the appointment of sufficiently large numbers of trained and armed game wardens is usually financially impossible.

Conservation can sometimes be achieved by providing animals with necessities they themselves have difficulty finding. We can help many animals increase their numbers by providing relatively simple contrivances such as salt licks for ungulates; suitable nesting sites for various birds (hanging nests for swallows, washtubs or garbage cans on stilts for Canada geese), as well as by preserving small patches of woodland as sources of food and shelter for various small animal forms. Further important measures for preserving animal populations are the creation of small pools as amphibian spawning grounds and the maintenance of larger marsh or wetland areas as breeding grounds and resting places for migrating waterfowl (Fig. 60). The most extensive work in this latter field has been accomplished in western Canada by Ducks Unlimited, a private non-profit organization dedicated to preserving and developing waterfowl breeding habitat. Operating primarily in Canada but supported almost entirely by funds contributed by American sportsmen, the organization is an excellent example of international cooperation to conserve wildlife resources.

At the beginning of 1964, Ducks Unlimited had built and was maintaining approximately 644 active waterfowl projects, primarily in the Canadian prairie region. The total water area involved was about 1,000,000 acres with a total shoreline mileage of more than 6,000 miles. Water conservation in suitable areas has been the company's main

Fig. 60. Marshland in southern France. Such reed and marsh areas play an important role in the water relations of a region, and also as resting spots for migrating birds. *Photo by B. Gagnaire/World Wildlife Fund.*

objective. They have accomplished this largely by preserving and stabilizing existing marshes and potholes, but in several instances they have created artificial marshes where none previously existed. Their activities have not, however, been confined entirely to water management and the construction of dams, dikes, and ditches. Several areas have been fenced to protect the nesting cover and emergent plants from hungry livestock. Food plants such as smart weed and sago pondweed as well as emergent cover plants such as bulrushes have been planted along shorelines, in open marshes, and on topsides and edges of earth-fill dams. Planting on dams has the dual advantage of reducing erosion and providing cover for the birds. Shallow areas which have become too overgrown with emergent plants, particularly cattail, have been partly cleared by burning and mowing. Although these projects are designed to benefit waterfowl, on occasion the principal benefits are received by fish, amphibians, or small fur bearers. It is a demonstrated fact that such projects also benefit adjacent human communities in the sense of available water reserves.

Not all our conservation efforts are as successful or meaningful. For example, hanging out starling nest-boxes simply brings an unpleasant and unwanted increase in the numbers of this species. In the sense of nature conservation, winter feeding of song birds with millet and sunflower seeds is also an ineffectual measure as such feeding benefits primarily the sparrows, green finches, and chaffinches who find sufficient natural food at this time of year. Cold and snow bring far greater difficulties to other bird species, especially hawks, eagles, and owls whom we can effectively help through winter's hardships by providing them with slaughterhouse refuse. Success in our efforts to preserve and protect any of nature's elements depends largely upon our ability to determine the biological consequences of our actions before we undertake them.

The classical method of nature protection through conservation is the establishment of reserves. We differentiate several types of reserves: partial reserves, such as those areas protected only during the breeding season; plant reserves in which the picking of plants is forbidden; game refuges where hunting is not allowed; and total reserves in which the plants, animals, and the entire landscape are protected.

Reserves can fulfill an important role. As the initial step in nature conservation, they offer decimated animal populations opportunity to recover and rebuild themselves. Ideally, because life in reserves proceeds largely undisturbed, a regular surplus of animals is produced which may wander out into the surrounding unprotected areas. In this sense, reserves serve as a source and reservoir of animals for the hunters. Further, reserves permit the study of game animals under natural conditions and thus help provide better foundations for game management. Finally, in many places reserves represent tourist attractions, and especially in underdeveloped lands can provide an important source of foreign funds. For these various reasons it is desirable to clothe our earth with as dense a network of reserves as is possible (Fig. 61).

It is, however, a fatal mistake to believe that reserves provide the ultimate answer or that we can create a reserve and then forget it with the rationalization that nature will find its own way. The erroneous view that man serves the cause of conservation best when he hermetically seals an area from his own influences is especially well preserved among the older generation of nature conservationists. Actually, it has been

Fig. 61. Map of African game reserves and National Parks.

clearly illustrated that reserves must be supervised and managed by a
scientifically competent authority, and that when necessary man must
extend his influence to regulate any upset balance. A short example
from the Frisian Islands will serve to demonstrate this point. Certain
areas on these islands were declared totally protected zones for the
birds nesting there. Soon after this declaration it became apparent that
the herring gull, arch nest robber, was benefiting most by the action,
increasing rapidly, and becoming a danger to all other birds in the area.
It became necessary to protect the nesting birds not by keeping them
totally unsullied by man's influence, but by actively waging war on the
herring gull. In the Swiss National Park, whose sacrosanct nature is
guaranteed by the government, decisive action must sooner or later be
taken to reduce the red deer population which is increasing without
control and threatening to destroy the Park's vegetation.

Numerous European marsh and heath areas cannot be left "protected"

and excluded from man's influence. When the plants in these areas are
neither mowed nor grazed by sheep every year, a few decades see
their end and the beginnings of a young forest. Most of the marshes
and heaths are not natural landscapes. They owe their unique structure
and life forms directly or indirectly to man's activities. Before man's
influence these areas were largely covered by forest. Such was true for
the famous Lünenburg heath. Several decades ago sheepherding in that
region became increasingly less rewarding and the practice gradually
fell into disuse. As the sheep disappeared so did the fragrant, rose seas
of heather, and monotonous unbroken stands of pine took their place
(Fig. 62). In the final and most successful attempt to preserve a portion

Fig. 62. Lüneburg heath. The encroaching forest is visible in the
background. *Photo by V. Ziswiler.*

of the vanishing heath, sheep were reintroduced to the reserve and
allowed to continue their necessary maintenance work. The annual
mowing of the marsh grasses or the grazing of the moors were necessary
for their creation and now are indispensable prerequisites for the
preservation of these landscapes.

The reasons why we must continually supervise our reserves and
occasionally effect corrections and guide their development include the
following. As just mentioned, many reserves are established to preserve
interesting and valuable but nevertheless unnatural landscapes that owe
their existence and biological balance to the efforts of man. Often these
biocoenoses were damaged at the time of their creation. Man has shifted

their biological balance, and until they achieve a new state of equilibrium man must continually intervene and help guide their development. In the case of many European game preserves, essential elements of the fauna, particularly sufficient numbers of carnivores, were absent at the time of their establishment. Now the herbivores increase at unnaturally high rates and cause excessive damage to the plant life.

Most European reserves are too small to exist as autonomous, self-regulating units. The influence of the neighbouring unnatural areas extends too far into these reserves for a natural balance to develop. Too small to maintain natural carnivores, the equilibrium of such reserves is further upset by the immigration of wild-running cats and dogs from the neighbouring areas.

Maintaining and Breeding Threatened Animal Forms in Captivity

The last hope for preserving gravely threatened animal species lies in the attempt to maintain and breed these in captivity. In this respect, zoological gardens have many encouraging successes to record. Today some animal species exist *only* in captivity or on preserves. An example is Père David's deer (*Elaphurus davidianus*), a large deer species discovered in the Imperial Gardens of Peking by the Lazarist missionary, Père Armand David, in 1861 (Fig. 63). Although at the time of its discovery this deer species was already extinct in the wild, it now lives in numerous zoos throughout the world.

Fig. 63. Père David's deer. *Photo by V. Ziswiler.*

Other famous captive-bred populations are those of the European buffalo and the Asiatic wild horse (*Equus przewalski*). In 1923 a society was formed to preserve the European buffalo (Fig. 64), and an inter-

Fig. 64. European buffalo. *Photo by M. Meyer-Holzapfel/World Wildlife Fund.*

national buffalo stud book was established. Thanks to this energetic concern for the species' future, the buffalo stand had increased to 100 pure-blooded animals by 1939. Since 1929 the primeval forests of Bialowieza, Poland have been inhabited by wild buffalo, 15 of which managed to survive the Second World War. Based on these remaining animals a new breeding program was initiated, and a special research station for European buffalo was organized under the direction of K. Krysiak. By 1952 the first buffalo from the new enclosures could be released in the wild. Today more than 50 buffalo inhabit the Bialowieza forest.

A similar breeding program distributed over many zoos was pursued with the Asiatic wild horse (Fig. 65). This species was discovered in

Fig. 65. The Asiatic wild horse. *Photo by V. Ziswiler.*

1897 by the Russian officer and explorer Przewalski in Mongolia, and is the only living representative of the original wild horse. Its home was the high steppes of the Dsungari where a few individuals may still survive. While the wild population struggles to maintain itself, a successful breeding program dating to the turn of the century when the first animals were brought back by Hagenbeck has been accomplished with the captive stock. On January 1, 1964 about 110 wild horses were alive in captivity—far more than still exist in the wild state.

In 1951 the native population of the Hawaiian goose (*Branta sandvicensis*, Fig. 66) had sunk to only 30 individuals. These last animals were evacuated and held in captivity. Under the direction of Peter Scott of the Severn Wildfowl Trust in England, a breeding program was instituted with the captive population. The action was so successful that by 1964 the captive population had increased to 389 animals and the geese have now been re-established on Hawaii.

Lately, very promising beginnings have been made with the breeding of several rare animals—the great Indian rhino, the Orang-utan, the gorilla, and only recently, the Arabian oryx. The largest captive population of the oryx, only about a dozen animals, now resides far from its Arabian home in a Phoenix, Arizona zoo.

Private animal owners can also perform a worthwhile service in the maintenance of threatened species. Numerous rare Australian parakeets of the genera *Psephotus, Neophema,* and *Platycercus,* such as the hooded, paradise, and turquoise parakeets, which are already partially extinct

Fig. 66. Hawaiian goose. *Photo by F. Vollmar/World Wildlife Fund.*

in their native land are being maintained and bred in the cages of private bird lovers. It is certainly important that such private breeders of rare animals organize themselves and enact mutual population controls for the vanishing species.

Nature Protection Through Restoration

Nature protection through restoration attempts to re-establish states of nature that previously existed. In greatest need for such rehabilitation are our natural water systems. Reforestation and the reintroduction of certain animal species to their original environment are also important phases in the restoration of nature.

One of the most remarkable examples of a successful animal reintroduction is the reinstatement of the alpine ibex (Fig. 67) in the Swiss Alps. This imposing alpine game species was already exterminated

Fig. 67. Male alpine ibex. *Photo by A. Rauch.*

through most of the Alps in the 18th century. By 1850 the last ibex had disappeared from the Valais region—and the animal was extinct in Switzerland. Only in the northwest corner of Italy, in the Aosta valley near Mt. Blanc, were a few individuals able to survive. Fortunately the ibex of this mountainous area were protected first by the Piemontese government in 1821, and later by the Italian kings who made the area their royal hunting reserve. After the founding of the Italian republic this reserve was converted to the Gran Paradiso National Park.

During the 19th century, numerous well meant attempts were made to re-establish the ibex in Switzerland. These attempts, mostly involving hybrids between the ibex and domestic goat, failed largely because the hybrid kids were born too early in the spring. The first release of pure-blooded ibex was also a failure. At the beginning of this century the St. Gallen Animal Park Association decided to take matters into its own hands. After initial failures with hybrid goats and difficulties in obtaining pure ibex from Italy, the first three ibex kids were smuggled over the Swiss-Italian border in 1906. Later legal purchases increased the original breeding stock to 34 animals. These animals were bred in enclosures before any attempts to release them in the wild were risked. In 1911 the first of this stock was released in the mountains of St. Gallen. Of the subsequent releases a few failed; the majority, however, led to successful re-establishment.

The most successful colonies developed so favourably that they soon became "mother colonies" and supplied animals for further reintroductions. Since their establishment, the three large colonies in Grisons, Berne, and Valais together have yielded more than 1,000 animals to be released in other areas. Presently there are about 40 established ibex colonies in the Swiss mountains, totalling more than 3,700 animals. Through emigration or conscious efforts by man, ibex bred in Switzerland are now enriching the alpine regions of several other countries including Austria, Jugoslavia, France, and even Italy.

A similar success story comes from the mountains of western North America. A not so distant relative of the ibex, the California bighorn sheep (*Ovis canadensis californicus*) had been almost completely exterminated in the United States. Sheep captured in Canada were bred in enclosures and later successfully re-established in the mountains of Washington and Oregon.

The most important prerequisite to the successful re-establishment of an animal in its original range is the presence of suitable habitat. Many areas have been significantly altered since the times when their natural fauna was still abundant, and by no means all animals are sufficiently adaptable to be reintroduced into such modified environments. The reintroduction of the wolf to central Europe is unthought of, and it is questionable whether there still is enough suitable habitat in the Alps to allow the re-establishment of the bear. To be sure, the bear leads a significantly more sedentary life than the wolf, but it places great nutritional demands on its environment. In particular, bears require extensive berry patches and sufficient winter kill in spring to avoid a hunger-directed shift to domestic animals.

Of all the larger European carnivores, the lynx could be most easily reintroduced. Although it requires expansive forest areas, the lynx feeds primarily upon birds and small mammals. An exceptionally shy and withdrawn animal, the lynx would never annoy, let alone menace, man as is feared by many people.

Wildlife Management

As an inhabitant of this earth man has a legitimate claim to the utilization of nature and her products—this we must not forget. Man is not, however, permitted to use nature's resources excessively as this simply results in their, and ultimately his, destruction. It is therefore among the duties of modern nature protection to investigate and propagate all possibilities for the efficient, continuing utilization of nature. The protection of nature has entered a new phase. A distinct separation between man and nature is no longer expounded; rather, man is regarded as an integral part of nature who must adjust his activities to those of the rest of nature's household in such manner that all members benefit. This dynamic integrated protection and utilization of nature is the way of the future.

Modern forestry is currently adopting this common sense approach to its utilization of nature. For several decades man has recognized that, in the long run, unnaturally simple forests bring more disadvantages than advantages, and in many places he has therefore decided to convert such monocultures to more natural conditions. Logging and silvicultural methods have been altered. In place of the formerly popular, but often soil destroying, clear-cut system, man is increasingly using the more natural shelterwood and selection systems. The former system creates small sheltered clearings in which natural regeneration takes place. The latter system or selection forest is the most natural form of a high forest as felling is limited to individual trees distributed over the entire forest, and the natural regeneration takes place in numerous scattered spots. Over extended periods this form of utilization provides a greater yield and a larger area of natural forest habitat (Figs. 68 and 69). Clear-cut systems, however, will never be completely replaced by more refined systems, as in certain areas clear-cutting approximates natural conditions more closely. For thousands of years nature has been effecting clear cuts through avalanches, rock and mud slides, insect epidemics, violent storms, and lightning fires. As some game species, particularly deer and grouse, benefit greatly from the creation of open areas, small scale clear cut logging will always remain a useful tool of the wildlife manager.

One of the oldest methods of managing our wildlife is that employed by the inland fisheries. Reductions in the output of fish eggs are compensated for by the release of young fish artificially raised in hatcheries. Utilization of various other animal populations has received ever increasing attention since the Second World War. North America

Fig. 68. Clear cut in Württemberg. The soil of the clear-cut area is completely exposed to the ravages of wind and water. Fortunately such coarse logging methods are becoming less frequent. *Photo by A. Kurth, FVA, Birmensdorf.*

and the Soviet Union have been the pioneers and together have laid the foundations for biological game management. From North America have come trail blazing works on the biology of several game animals including the pronghorn antelope (*Antilocapra americana*), the bighorn sheep, the caribou, and several waterfowl species. Studies such as these provide the necessary basis for successful management of animal populations.

A wide range of various fur bearers are being effectively managed in

Fig. 69. Selection forest. This is the most natural form of forest management. Different ages and species of trees are mingled among and over each other. The utilization of a selection forest is based upon single trees scattered over the entire forest area. *Photo by A. Kurth, FVA, Birmensdorf.*

the Soviet Union. For several years now Soviet hunters have again been able to harvest the once rare sea otter. In Norway the relatively small beaver population of 14,000 animals is so efficiently managed that a considerable number of beavers can be utilized yearly without adversely affecting the population.

The first large scale management of a wild herd-animal (other than the Lapland reindeer which should be considered domestic) was accomplished by the Russians with the saiga, *Saiga tatarica* (Fig. 70). As a consequence of the great demand for its flesh and horns, this antelope of the Asiatic steppes was almost completely exterminated by the 19th century. In 1919 the species was placed under complete protection.

Between 1940 and 1950 Russian scientists conducted a comprehensive study on the biology of this species in which the most important questions regarding food plants, migrations, and stand structure could be answered. Encouraged by appropriate protective measures, the saiga population increased from about 1,000 animals in 1930 to about 2,500,000 in 1960. By 1950 the utilization of the stand had begun. Today special hunting brigades kill 250,000 to 350,000 saigas annually and thereby

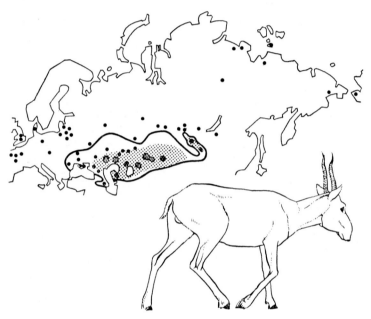

Fig. 70. Saiga antelope. Black points indicate fossil finds; the striped areas represent the distribution in 1920; the stippled area represents the present distribution. *After A. G. Bannikov.*

obtain 6,600 tons of excellent meat, 240,000 square yards of leather, and large amounts of fat and other raw materials for the chemical industry. To avoid any permanent decrease in the population, the herd's utilization and management are continually supervised by a scientific team.

The management of sea bird colonies has recently become the object of exhaustive biological studies. Particularly the Japanese and Russians are interested in this possibility of utilizing nature's resources. We know that 50 to 60 per cent of all eggs in such colonies meet an early end through various factors such as rat predation or disturbance of the brooding parents. If man can eliminate a portion of this early mortality, he can utilize a greater number of the eggs himself without threatening the continued existence of the species concerned. It has also been demonstrated that the breeding densities of these colonies can be increased through such simple measures as clearing the rock debris from the cliffs and crags used as breeding grounds. Under these conditions, bird breeding grounds can be expediently managed and up to 40 per cent of the first laying can be collected without endangering the birds. In Newfoundland where the bird colonies are managed primarily for their flesh, the expected average harvest is 300,000 to 500,000 birds per year.

In Michigan, U.S.A. a small warbler and its habitat are being intensively managed for an entirely different purpose. We have already mentioned the plight of Kirtland's warbler in our discussion of indirect extermination. The warbler or jack pine bird currently nests exclusively in a small, sandy, sun-scorched, fire-scarred plains area in central Michigan appropriately known as "the barrens." The specialized forest type growing there is created only through fire. A ground nesting species, Kirtland's warbler nests where the living jack pine boughs reach down into the grass and blueberry bushes, concealing its eggs and young from predators. The pines must be young, 5 to 20 years old; short, 6 to 18 feet tall; and sufficiently scattered that even the lower branches receive sunlight and remain alive. Before man controlled them, lightning fires provided a continuous supply of the suitable young-growth, jack pine habitat. Man's efficiency at fire control now threatens to eliminate the warbler's home and push it over the brink of extinction. To save the species man has had to assume nature's role and burn the forests himself. Unlike nature's, however, these burnings are controlled and confined to the Kirtland's Warbler Management Area. The management areas were established to ensure that future generations will also hear and see the little, yellow-breasted warbler. To accomplish this objective about one square mile of the pine forests within the areas' confines is burned every five years. Where the fire doesn't encourage the sprouting of sufficient pine seedlings the areas are selectively planted.

As well as being truly unique, the only forest area especially managed to preserve a song bird, the Kirtland's Warbler Management Area provides an excellent example of the integrated management and utilization of our resources. It is not a preserve or inviolate wildlife sanctuary, but is *managed* for four resources. Timber is cut according to a prescribed management plan. The foresters mark certain trees which remain to provide the necessary seed after controlled burning. Hunting, berry-picking, and general recreation are permitted and enjoyed. Protection is given to watershed values involved. But the primary purpose of the management area remains to provide the Kirtland's warbler's specialized nesting site and to preserve its distinctive liquid song for posterity.

It is the management of African game, however, that has become the most important and fateful issue of nature protection. In Africa as everywhere else, the promotion of protection for game populations must be based on factual as well as idealistic arguments. One possibility for the utilization of African animal life and game preserves is tourism, which brings important foreign funds to these lands. In 1959 tourism brought East Africa earnings of £22,000,000. In South Africa, Kruger Park alone yielded a net profit of £59,160 in 1960.

For several years science has been concerned with the problem of finding other ways to utilize Africa's wild game herds. To help answer this question, two Americans, F. Dasman and A. S. Mossman, set up a large experiment. A 138,000 acre tract of arable land in South Africa was chosen for the experiment. Half of this area was "cultivated" and opened to herds of domestic cattle; the other half was left as the wilderness home of a mixed herd of 15 different wild game species. After some time a portion of both populations was harvested leaving enough animals so that the continued existence of neither herd was endangered. The 1,100 wild animals obtained in this way yielded flesh which was sold to the local population and hides which were sold on the export markets. In the final comparison, the revenue from the wild mixed herd exceeded that from the domestic herd by about 25 per cent. This and later experiments demonstrate that the wild game populations in Africa provide a greater revenue and better utilization of natural resources than do domestic animals reared under the same conditions.

The reasons for the wild game's superiority include the following.

1. In contrast to wild game, cattle herds are very susceptible to tropical livestock diseases such as trypanosomiasis, the tsetse fly-spread sleeping sickness. It is estimated that during the last few decades at least 34,000 tons of domestic cattle flesh have been lost through the activities of this little fly.

2. The wild game is more resistant to heat and drought. Every year thousands of cattle die in areas where wild game survives relatively unscathed.

3. Wild game herds are composed of a multitude of widely differentiated forms with different habits and requirements; hence they are able to utilize the vegetation more fully and evenly than can the domestic herds. Giraffes and elephants browse the upper layers of the foliage; hippos feed on the river-bank vegetation; rhinos utilize various shrubs, and zebras and antelopes graze on the grasses of the steppes (Fig. 71). Thus wild game cannot only exploit zones of vegetation that are inaccessible to domestic animals, but can also avoid making excessive

demands on any single layer or zone of the vegetation. Simple, unmixed cattle herds eat their way head to head through the grass layer, grazing the area bald and thus paving the way for erosion and ultimate destruction of the soil.

4. As wild game has evolved along with or within the environment, it is better adapted and faster growing than the imported domestic stock. In an area where eland antelope achieve a respectable average weight of 700 pounds, the entire cattle population may starve (Fig. 72).

The facts are so convincing that in South Africa many settlers are already converting their husbandry from cattle to wild game. On many of the giant ranches, often comprising thousands of acres, cattle graze no longer; in their place gnus, zebras, and antelope grace the landscape. In 1959 more than 3,500 tons of wild game meat were sold in Transvaal. Today in that area alone 3,000 settlers are managing game herds. For the African nation, wildlife management has become an economic factor of the first magnitude. For large areas of Africa, wildlife management provides the most efficient utilization of resources and can help remedy the chronic protein deficiency suffered by most of the nation's inhabitants. A human requires an average of about 80 grams of protein daily. Of this, 30 grams should be of animal origin. The populace of East Africa, however, receives an average daily protein ration of 56 grams, of which only 5 grams is of animal origin. The hides that are harvested with the meat provide the Africans with further valuable products.

Today wildlife management projects are underway in practically all parts of Africa. Mastering the many problems as they come to light is by no means easy because a satisfactory game management program requires the fulfillment of certain essential prerequisites. Comprehensive research work must be completed to provide a thorough understanding of the biology of the species to be utilized and to establish the harvest quotas. Game populations must be continually regulated during their utilization. Furthermore, we must recognize that we cannot utilize an animal population without damaging it unless we simultaneously implement measures to increase the population. In Africa it is relatively simple to recognize possibilities for increasing the populations' numbers. There the main problem for most of the gregarious or herd-forming animals is water (Fig. 73). Simply by constructing artificial watering places we can promote population increases to such an extent that we easily compensate for the losses created by our utilization. It is therefore, contrary to common belief, not necessary to decimate the ungulates' natural enemies, the carnivores.

A further important requisite for satisfactory management is the efficient organization of product disposal. Economical capture and killing methods must be developed to obtain the harvestable animals without

a)

Fig. 71. African wild game makes efficient use of the vegetation.
(a) Black rhino browses bushes and shrubs.

b)

(b) Giraffe utilizes the tree crowns.

c)

(c) Grant's gazelles graze the grass layer.

d)

(d) Elephant feeds on tree foliage. *Photos by C. A. W. Guggisberg/World Wildlife Fund.*

a)

b)

Fig. 72. Comparison of wild and domestic animals in Africa.
(a) Where wild game flourishes, (b) the cattle languish. *Photos by
C. A. W. Guggisberg/World Wildlife Fund and Kenya Information
Dept./World Wildlife Fund.*

Fig. 73. Buffalo herd at a watering hole. Sufficient watering spots are among the most important requirements for successful management of African game. *Photo by C. A. W. Guggisberg/World Wildlife Fund.*

unduly disturbing the herd. In tropical Africa it is essential that the meat be rapidly disposed of. It must either reach the consumer very quickly, or be immediately frozen; both alternatives represent complex technical problems.

A great deal of demonstration and explanation is still necessary to convince the Africans that their large game populations are a precious national resource. For this purpose a staff of native scientists, supervisory personnel, and administrative officials must be trained and instituted.

The eastern and central African steppes and savannas are especially well suited for wildlife management. These areas support the greatest biomass yet observed on earth.

COMPARISON OF THE BIOMASS OF VARIOUS ZONES
Biomass measured in number of kilograms of animal substance per square kilometer

Asia	Kirghiz steppes (saiga antelope)	350 kg
North America	North Canada (caribou)	800 kg
Europe	Scottish Highlands (red deer)	1,000 kg
Africa	Deserts (Sahara, Kalihari)	0.3–190 kg
	Savanna (South Kivu)	2,000–3,000 kg
	Acacia savanna (Kenya)	15,000 kg
	Moist savanna (Uganda, East Congo)	18,000–31,000 kg

UNESCO commissions and various other international organizations for the conservation of natural beauty and wildlife have drafted recommendations for the management of Africa's nature. One of their proposals is the division of African territories into three zones, as follows.

1. Cultural zones: areas best suited for utilization by man, especially through agriculture and industry. In these areas the animals are not protected and may be slain or expelled.

2. Wildlife management zones: here both wild and domestic animal herds are managed. These zones must be closely supervised to avoid destruction of the biological balance.

3. Natural zones: (a) Reserves and parks with stringent protection and without human settlement. (b) Forest areas with limited utilization by the forest dwelling native tribes. (c) Rivers, lakes and marshes whose flora and fauna are protected, but can be utilized under certain stipulations for fishing and crocodile or hippo capture.

Proposals concerning the detailed distribution of natural, management, and cultural zones recommended that natural and cultural zones should never be directly adjacent, but should be separated by a buffer or management zone (Fig. 74).

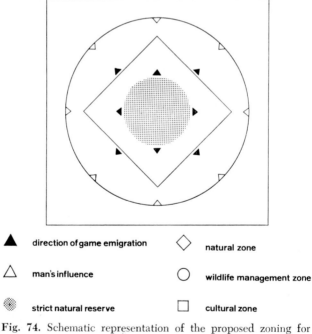

▲ direction of game emigration   ◇ natural zone

△ man's influence   ○ wildlife management zone

▒ strict natural reserve   □ cultural zone

Fig. 74. Schematic representation of the proposed zoning for managing Africa's game.

The concern for wildlife management has already begun to manifest encouraging success. The utilization of the Lake Edward and Lake George hippo populations began in 1958 and it appears that these areas will supply about 1,000 animals annually on a sustained yield basis. Their exceptionally tender and protein rich meat is sold to the natives. The calculated annual meat yield from Moore's antelope in Northern Rhodesia is about 4½ million pounds; a similar game utilization project is being prepared for the Kob antelope on the Semiliki flats. Finally in Murchison Falls National Park an attempt is being made to harvest the 12,000 strong elephant herd on a sustained yield basis of about 1,000 animals per year.

In Closing

After the shattering and discouraging truth which we have seen in the last chapters, it is with a certain relief that we confirm modern nature-protection's command over effective methods to oppose nature's destruction without obstructing mankind's development. The most excellent knowledge, however, is of no use unless it is universally and energetically converted to action; unless the concept of nature protection becomes a part of the general good; and unless governments recognize that nature protection in its ultimate end is mankind's protection. Propagation of the nature protection ideal lies in the hands of national and international organizations of which two deserve our special attention: the International Union for the Conservation of Nature and Natural Resources (IUCN), and the World Wildlife Fund (WWF). These two organizations complement each other in that IUCN conducts research in nature protection, attempts to increase the numbers of various animal populations, and plans protective measures, while WWF under the symbol of the giant panda coordinates these propositions and attempts to procure the necessary financial resources.

The activities of different nature conservation organizations have already achieved encouraging successes. Essential prerequisites for effective protective measures are being fulfilled; for example, the editing of the "red book" by the IUCN's Survival Services Commission. The "red book" contains all available data concerning the populations of threatened species and the nature of the threat to the population. Revisions and additions to it are continually being made whenever new information becomes available. In various lands, such as Switzerland and West Germany, an inventory of all landscapes of national and international significance is being made, and the measures for their protection discussed. Under so-called project MAR all the significant reed and marsh-

lands of Europe were registered and the way for their protection prepared. The greatest success of this project was without a doubt the
protection of the 625,000 acre Spanish Guadalquivir delta area. Thanks
to the initiative of the WWF and the willingness of the Spanish government to cooperate, the unique flora and fauna of this natural landscape
have been placed under total protection.

This and similar successes throughout the world justify our hopes for
a brighter future; however, they represent only a minute portion of all
the protective measures actually necessary to effectively oppose the
increasing impoverishment of nature and particularly the further extermination of animal forms.

Appendices

Compiled from Allen (1942), Harper (1945), Greenway (1958), and IUCN Bulletins (1964).

Key to Symbols:

Hunted for meat or fat	A
Hunted for hides or feathers	B
Hunted for trophies or souvenirs	C
Hunted for sport or pleasure	D
Eggs and young collected	E
Captured for live-animal trade	F
Persecuted because of superstitious beliefs	G
Combatted as an alleged pest	H
Habitat altered through destruction of the forest	I
Habitat altered through drainage	K
Habitat altered through civilization or monocultures	L
Denaturalized fauna through goats or sheep	M
Denaturalized fauna through rabbits	N
Denaturalized fauna through feral dogs	O
Denaturalized fauna through feral cats	P
Denaturalized fauna through feral pigs	Q
Denaturalized fauna through rats	R
Denaturalized fauna through foxes	S
Denaturalized fauna through mongoose forms	T
Denaturalized fauna through mustelids (weasel, European polecat)	U
Destroyed by introduced animal diseases	V

Appendix I

LIST OF BIRD AND MAMMAL FORMS ALREADY EXTINCT

Two-figure numbers give the century of the extinction; four-figure numbers, the year in which the last individual disappeared.

Birds

Ostriches

Arabian ostrich Struthio camelus syriacus	Saudi Arabia	20 D

Emus

Tasmanian emu Dromaius novaehollandiae diemenensis	Tasmania	19 H
Kangaroo Island emu Dromaius novaeahollandiae diemeniamus	Kangaroo Island	19 I

Petrels

Guadalupe storm petrel Oceanodroma macrodactyla	Guadalupe	20 P

Cormorants

Spectacled cormorant Phalacrocorax perspicillatus	Bering Island	1852 B E

Hawks

Guadalupe Island caracara Polyborus lutosus	Guadalupe	1900 H M

Herons

Bonin night heron Nycticorax caledonicus crassirostris	Bonin Islands	1889 L P

Ducks

Indian pink-headed duck Rhodonessa caryophyllacea	India	1940 A
Coues's gadwall Anas strepera couesi	Washington Island	19 L
Labrador duck Camptorhynchus labradorius	Eastern North America	1875 A L
Auckland Island merganser Mergus australis	Auckland Islands	1901 R A
Crested shelduck Tadorna cristata	Korea	1916 A B

Quails and Partridges

New Zealand quail Coturnix novae-zelandiae novae-zelandiae	New Zealand	19 V
Himalaya quail Ophrysia superciliosa	Himalaya	19 A
Heath hen Tympanuchus cupido cupido	Eastern U.S.A.	1932 I D

Cuckoos

Delalande's Madagascar Coucal Coua delalandei	Madagascar	20 L

Rails

Red-billed rail Rallus pacificus	Tahiti	19 R P
Jamaica wood rail Amaurolimnas concolor concolor	Jamaica	1881 T
Chatham Island banded rail Rallus dieffenbachii	Chatham Island	19 P R
Wake Island rail Rallus wakensis	Wake Island	20 A
Auckland Island rail Rallus muelleri	Auckland Islands	19 P
Chatham Island rail Cabalus modestus	Chatham Island	19 M N
Laysan Island rail Porzanula palmeri	Laysan Island	20 R
Hawaiian rail Pennula sandwichensis	Hawaii	19 T
Kusaie Island crake Aphanolimnas monasa	Kusaie Island	19 R

Fiji bar-winged rail Nesoclopeus poeciloptera	Viti Levu	20 T
Samoa wood rail Pareudiastes pacificus	Samoa	20 P R
Mauritian rail Aphanapteryx bonasia	Mauritius	17 A
Iwo Jima rail Poliolimnas cinereus brevipes	Iwo Jima	20 R P
Tristan Island Gallinule Gallinula nesiotis nesiotis	Tristan da Cunha	19 O
White swamp hen Porphyrio albus	Lord Howe Island	19 A

Shorebirds

Tahitian sandpiper Prosobonia leucoptera	Tahiti	19 Q
Eskimo curlew Numenius borealis	North America	20 A L

Auks

Great auk Alca impennis	North Atlantic	1844 E

Pigeons

Mauritius blue pigeon Alectroenas nitidissima	Mauritius	18 A
New Zealand pigeon Hemiphaga novaeseelandiae spadicea	Norfolk Island	19 L
Choiseul crested pigeon Microgoura meeki	Choiseul Island	20 P
Passenger pigeon Ectopistes migratorius	Eastern North America	1914 A D I
Puerto Rican blue pigeon Columba inornata wetmorei	Puerto Rico	20 L
Bonin wood pigeon Columba versicolor	Bonin Islands	20 P
Dodo Raphus cucullatus	Mauritius	17 A Q

Parrots

Norfolk Island parrot Nestor meridionalis productus	Norfolk Island	19 H
Guadeloupe parrot Amazona violacea	Guadeloupe	18
Culebra Island parrot Amazona vittata graciliceps	Culebra Island	20 F L

Cuba red macaw Ara tricolor	Cuba	19	F H
Puerto Rico Conure Aratinga chloroptera maugei	Puerto Rico	19	L
Carolina parakeet Conuropsis carolinensis	Southeastern U.S.A.	20	H
Mascarene parrot Mascarinus mascarinus	Réunion	19	I
Seychelles Alexandrine parakeet Psittacula eupatria wardi	Seychelles	19	I
Rodriguez ring-necked parakeet Psittacula krameri exsul	Rodriguez	20	I
Mauritius broad-billed parrot Lophopsittacus mauritianus	Mauritius	17	A
Rodriguez parakeet Necropsittacus rodericanus	Rodriguez	17	A
New Caledonian lorikeet Vini diadema	New Caledonia	20	I
Lord Howe Island kakariki Cyanoramphus novaezelandiae subflavescens	Lord Howe Island	19	H
Macquarie Island kakariki Cyanoramphus novaezelandiae erythrotis	Macquarie Island	20	P
Tahiti parakeet Cyanoramphus zelandicus	Tahiti	19	L
Raiatea parakeet Cyanoramphus ulietanus	Society Islands	18	

Owls

Rodriguez little owl Athene murivora	Rodriguez	17	L
Guadeloupe burrowing owl Speotyto cunicularia guadeloupensis	Maria Galante Island	19	T
Antigua burrowing owl Speotyto cunicularia amaura	Antigua and Nevis Islands	19	T
North Island laughing owl Sceloglaux albifacies rufifacies	New Zealand	19	L U
Seychelles Island owl Otus insularis	Seychelles	20	L

Nighthawks

Puerto Rican nighthawk Caprimulgus vociferus noctitherus	Puerto Rico	20	T

Jamaica Pauraque Siphonornis americanus americanus	Jamaica	19 P T

Kingfishers

Ryukyu kingfisher Halcyon miyakoensis	Miyako Island	19

Woodpeckers

Guadalupe red-shafted flicker Colaptes cafer rufipileus	Guadalupe	20 M

Passerines

Stephen Island wren Xenicus lyalli	Stephen Island (New Zealand)	20 P
Guadeloupe wren Troglodytes musculus guadeloupensis	Guadeloupe	20 T
Martinique wren Troglodytes musculus martinicensis	Martinique	20 T
Guadeloupe Bewick's wren Thyromanes bewickii brevicauda	Guadeloupe	19 M
Lord Howe grey-headed blackbird Turdus poliocephalus vinitinctus	Lord Howe Island	20 P Q
Raiatea thrush Turdus ulietensis	Society Islands	18 P R
Kittlitz's thrush Zoothera terrestris	Bonin Islands	20 P R
Lanai thrush Phaeornis obscurus lanaiensis	Lanai Island	20 V
Molokai thrush Phaeornis obscurus rutha	Molokai Island	20 R V
Oahu thrush Phaeornis obscurus oahensis	Oahu Island	20 R
Laysan millerbird Acrocephalus familiaris familiaris	Laysan Island	20 L
Chatham Island fernbird Bowdleria rufescens	Pitt Island	19 L M
Long-legged warbler Trichocichla rufa	Viti Levu	19 L
Eyrean grass-wren Amytornis goyderi	Australia	20 P
Lord Howe Island grey warbler Gergyone igata insularis	Lord Howe Island	19 L

Tongatabu Tahiti Flycatcher Pomarea nigra tabuensis	Tahiti	20 L
Lord Howe Island flycatcher Rhipidura flabellifera cervina	Lord Howe Island	19 L
Chatham Island bellbird Anthornis melanura melanocephala	Chatham Island	19 R
Kioea Chaetoptila angustipluma	Hawaii	19 L
Oahu oo Moho apicalis	Hawaii	19 I
Hawaii oo Moho nobilis	Hawaii	20 I
Molokai oo Moho bishopi	Hawaii	20 I
Lord Howe Island white-eye Zosterops strenua	Lord Howe Island	20 I
Hawaiian honey-creepers: 16 forms Drepaniidae	Hawaii	19–20 I L P
Guadalupe rufous-sided towhee Pipilo erythrophthalmus consobrinus	Guadalupe	19 M
Bonin Island Grosbeak Chaunoproctus ferreirostris	Bonin Island	19 L
St. Christopher bullfinch Loxigilla portoricensis grandis	St. Christopher Island	20 P
Darwin's ground-finch Geospiza magnirostris magnirostris	Galapagos	19 F
Sao Thomé grosbeak weaver Neospiza concolor	Sao Thomé Island	19 L
Réunion fody Foudia bruante	Réunion	18 L
Bourbon crested starling Fregilupus varius	Réunion	19 L
Lord Howe Island starling Aplonis fuscus hullianus	Lord Howe Island	20 R
Kusaie starling Aplonis corvina	Kusaie Island (Caroline Islands)	20 R
Mysterious starling Aplonis mavornata	Society Islands	19
Huia Heteralocha acutirostris	New Zealand	20 I

Mammals

Marsupials

Freckled marsupial mouse Antechinus apicalis	Australia	20 L
Eastern barred bandicoot Perameles fasciata	Australia	20 P S
Western barred bandicoot Perameles myosura myosura	Australia	20 S P
Gaimard's rat-kangaroo Bettongia gaimardi	Australia	20 S P
Gilbert's rat-kangaroo Potorous gilberti	Australia	19 A
Broad-faced rat-kangaroo Potorous platyops	Australia	20 S P
Toolach wallaby Wallabia greyi	Australia	20 S
Tasmanian wolf Thylacinus cynocephalus	Tasmania	20 H

Insectivores

Antillean insectivores: 6 forms Nesophontidae	Antilles	17–19 R T
Christmas Island musk-shrew Crocidura fuliginosa trichura	Christmas Island	20 P

Bats

7 forms	West Indies	19–20 I

Lemurs

Hairy-eared mouse lemur Cheirogaleus trichotis	Madagascar	19 I

Rodents

Spiny rats: 15 forms Echimyidae	Antilles	17–20 T P
Hamsterlike rodents: 8 forms Cricetidae	Antilles	17–20 T P
Old World rats: 3 forms Muridae	Malay Archipelago and Australia	20 S P
Giant rats: 2 forms Dinomyidae	Central America and Antilles	19 A

Sea Cows

Steller's sea cow Hydrodamalis gigas	Bering Islands	1768 A

Carnivores

Sea mink Mustela macrodon	Northeast coast of the U.S.A.	19 B
Grizzly bear: 17 races Ursus horribilis	North America	19–20 A H
Atlas bear Ursus crowtheri	North Africa	19 A H I
Long-eared kit fox Vulpes macrotis macrotis	Southern U.S.A.	19 H
Japanese wolf Canis hodophilax	Japan	20 H
Antarctic wolf Dusicyon australis	Falkland Islands	19 H
Newfoundland wolf Canis lupus beothucus	Newfoundland	20 H
Florida wolf Canis niger niger	Florida	20 H
Eastern cougar Felis concolor couguar	Eastern U.S.A.	20 H
European lion Panthera leo europaea	Greece	1–2 O H
Cape lion Panthera leo melanochaitus	South Africa	1865 H
Barbary lion Panthera leo barbarus	North Africa	1922 H

Horses and relatives
(Perissodactyla)

Syrian wild ass Equus hemionus hemippus	Syria, Persia	1927 A
Algerian wild ass Equus asinus atlanticus	North Africa	?
Quagga Equus quagga	South Africa	1878 H
Burchell's zebra Equus burchelli burchelli	South Africa	20 H

Cattle and relatives
(Artiodactyla)

Arizona wapiti Cervus canadensis merriami	Arizona	1906 D I
Eastern wapiti Cervus canadensis canadensis	Eastern U.S.A.	19 I
Schomburgk's deer Rucervus schomburgki	Siam	20 G

Badlands bighorn sheep Ovis canadensis auduboni	American middle west	20 A D
Pyrenean ibex Capra pyrenaica pyrenaica	Pyrenees	1910 A
Portuguese ibex Capra pyrenaica lusitanica	Western Pyrenees	1892 A D
Rufous gazelle Gazella rufina	Algeria	20 A D
Blue buck Hippotragus leucophaeus	South Africa	19 H
Bubal Hartebeest Alcelaphus alcelaphus	North Africa	20 A
Auroch Bos primigenius	Europe	1627 A I
Eastern bison Bison bison pensylvanicus	North America	1825 A D
Oregon bison Bison bison oregonus	North America	19 A D
Caucasian wisent Bison bonasus caucasicus	Caucasus	1930 A I

Appendix II

LIST OF THE MOST GRAVELY THREATENED ANIMAL FORMS

Numbers in parentheses give the total number of threatened forms within each animal group; numbers without parentheses give the estimated number of individuals of that form which are still living.

Reptiles

Seychelles giant tortoise *Testudo gigantea*	Seychelles	A E
Galapagos giant tortoise *Testudo elephantopus*	Galapagos	A M P R
Green turtle *Chelonia mydas*	tropical seas	E A
Chinese alligator *Alligator sinensis*	lower course of the Yangtze-kiang R.	A B H
Marine iguana *Amblyrhynchus cristatus*	Galapagos	O P A
Land iguana *Conolophus subcristatus*	Galapagos	O P
Gila monster *Heloderma suspectum*	Arizona, U.S.A.	F
Mexican beaded lizard *Heloderma horridum*	Mexico	F
Komodo dragon *Varanus komodoensis*	Komodo Island	L 100–200
Two-banded monitor *Varanus salvator*	Malay Archipelago	A

Birds

Tinamous (2)	South America	A
Penguins (1)		
Galapagos penguin Sphenicus mendiculus	Galapagos	A E 5000
Grebes (5)		
Lake Atitlan grebe Podilymbus gigas	Guatemala	A E 200
Alaotra grebe Podiceps rufolavatus	Madagascar	I K
Petrels and Shearwaters (8)		
Newell's shearwater Puffinus puffinus newelli	Hawaii	T
Cahow Pterodroma cahow	Bermuda Islands	A Q R 50
Waved albatross Diomedea irrorata	Galapagos	O P 6000
Steller's albatross Diomedea albatrus	Torischima Island	B 45
Cormorants (3)		
Galapagos flightless cormorant Nannopterum harrisi	Galapagos	A E 3000
Birds of prey (16)		
Anjouan Island sparrowhawk Accipiter francesii pusillus	Anjouan Island	H I 1–10
Galapagos buzzard Buteo galapagoensis	Galapagos	H O 200
Cuban hook-billed kite Chondrohierax wilsonii	Cuba	H I
Everglade kite Rostrhamus sociabilis plumbeus	Florida	L 4–5
Spanish imperial eagle Aquila heliaca adalberti	Spain and North Africa	C H 100
Monkey-eating eagle Pithecophaga jefferyi	Philippines	F I 100
California condor Gymnogyps californianus	California	D H 60
Mauritius kestrel Falco punctatus	Mauritius	H 10–20
Seychelles kestrel Falco araea	Seychelles	H

Storks and ibises (3)

Korean white stork Ciconia ciconia boyciana	Korea, Japan	A K
Japanese crested ibex Nipponia nippon	Japan	A B I 12

Ducks and geese (13)

Hawaiian goose Branta sandvicensis	Hawaii	A 400
Cape Barren goose Cereopsis novae-hollandiae	Islands south of Australia	A 2000
Cuban tree duck Dendorcygna arborea	Antilles	A E
Campbell Island flightless teal Anas aucklandica nesiotis	Campbell Island	50
New Zealand brown teal Anas aucklandica chlorotis	New Zealand	A 1000
Auckland Island flightless teal Anas aucklandica aucklandica	Auckland Islands	A
Laysan duck Anas platyrhynchos laysanensis	Laysan	R N 500
Hawaiian duck Anas platyrhynchos wyvilliana	Hawaii	P R T 200

Brush turkeys (4)

Maleo Macrocephalon maleo	Celebes	A
Marianas megapode Megapodius lapérouse lapérouse	Marianas Islands	I P R
Palau megapode Megapodius lapérouse senex	Palau Islands	A I

Grouse, pheasants and quails (7)

Attwater's prairie chicken Tympanuchus cupido attwateri	Southern Texas	A L P 500
Masked bobwhite Colinus virginianus ridgwayi	Northwestern Mexico	L
Mikado pheasant Syrmaticus mikado	Formosa	A
Swinhoe's pheasant Lophura swinhoi	Formosa	A 400

Cranes and relatives (17)

Takahe Notornis mantelli	New Zealand	S T U 300

Hawaiian gallinule Gallinula chloropus sandvicensis	Hawaii	K P R 200
Jamaica black rail Laterallus jamaicensis jamaicensis	Cuba	P R T
Whooping crane Grus americana	Canada	K A 33
Manchurian crane Grus japonensis	Japan, Manchuria	K 30
Siberian white crane Grus leucogeranus	Siberia	A 100
Hooded crane Grus monacha	Japan and eastern U.S.S.R.	K A 1000
Kagu Rhynochetos jubatus	New Caledonia	O P Q R
Great Indian bustard Choriotis nigriceps	Central India	A I

Gulls and shorebirds (7)

New Zealand snipe: 2 forms Coenocorypha aucklandica	New Zealand	A R
New Zealand shore plover Thinornis novae-seelandiae	Chatham Islands	R P 140
Hawaiian stilt Himantopus himantopus knudseni	Hawaii	A K 200
Audouin's gull Larus audouinii	Morocco	A E 150

Pigeons (14)

Tooth-billed pigeon Didunculus strigirostris	Samoa	R P
Mindoro imperial pigeon Ducula mindorensis	Mindoro	
Chatham Island pigeon Hemiphaga novaeseelandiae chathamensis	Chatham Island	A I
Ryukyu wood pigeon Columba jouyi	Ryukyu Islands	I

Parrots (22)

Bahamas parrot Amazona leucocephala bahamensis	Bahamas	I
Puerto Rico parrot Amazona vittata vittata	Puerto Rico	A I 2000

St. Lucia parrot Amazona versicolor	St. Lucia Island	I
St. Vincent parrot Amazona guildingii	St. Vincent Island	I
Lesser Vasa parrot Coracopsis nigra barklyi	Praslin Island in Seychelles	I
Forbe's parakeet Cyanorhamphus auriceps forbesi	Mangare Island (New Zealand)	R N 100
Ground parrot: 3 forms Pezoporus wallicus	Australia	A L P S
Australian night parrot Geopsittacus occidentalis	Australia	L P R
Orange-bellied parakeet Neophema chrysogaster mab	Australia	F L
Turquoise parakeet Neophema pulchella	Southeastern Australia	F L
Cape York paradise parakeet Psephotus chrysopterygius chrysopterygius	Australia	F 250
Black-caped parakeet Psephotus chrysopterygius dissimilis	Arnhem Land (Australia)	F
Beautiful parakeet Psephotus pulcherrimus	Australia	F R
Mauritian ring-necked parakeet Psittacula echo	Mauritius	I
Owl-parrot Strigops habroptilus	New Zealand	I S R

Owls (8)

Puerto Rico short-eared owl Asio flammeus portoricensis	Puerto Rico	P T
New Zealand laughing owl Sceloglaux albifacies albifacies	New Zealand	P U

Nighthawks (6) — Antilles and Central America — T

Swifts (3)

Kingfishers and relatives (2)

Long-tailed ground roller Uratelornis chimaera	Madagascar	I

Woodpeckers (9)

Red-bellied woodpecker: 2 forms Melanerpes superciliaris	Bahamas	I

Cuban ivory-billed woodpecker Campephilus principalis bairdii	Cuba	I D 12
Ivory-billed woodpecker Campephilus principalis principalis	Florida	I
Tristam's woodpecker Dryocopus javensis richardsi	Korea	I

Passerines (135)

Euler's flycatcher Empidonax euleri johnstonei	Grenada	L
New Zealand bush wrens: 3 forms Acanthisittidae	New Zealand	I R U
Scrub birds: 3 forms Atrichornithidae	Australia	L R
Hawaiian crow Corvus tropicus	Hawaii	B 25–50
New Zealand wattle-birds: 4 forms Callaeidae	New Zealand	I P R U
Wrens: 6 forms Troglodytidae	Central America and Antilles	I T
Thrashers: 2 forms Mimidae	Antilles	R
Thrushes: 11 forms Turdidae	tropical islands	I R P T
Old World warblers: 3 forms Sylviidae	Australia, Seychelles	P I
Tahiti flycatcher Pomarea nigra nigra	Tahiti	L R
Seychelles black paradise flycatcher Terpsiphone corvina	Seychelles	P R I
Piopio: 2 forms Turnagra capensis	New Zealand	I R
Ponapé mountain starling Aplonis pelzelni	Ponapé Island (Carolines)	I
Rothschild's starling Leucopsar rothschildi	Bali	F
Honey-eaters: 4 forms Meliphagidae	Australia and New Zealand	L A
White-eyes: 3 forms Zosteropidae	Fernando Po (Carolines)	I
Hawaiian honey-creepers: 8 forms Drepaniidae	Hawaii	I L V

Wood warblers: 5 forms Parulidae	North and Central America	I L T
Weavers and relatives: 3 forms Ploceidae	Seychelles and Tristan da Cunha	I P
Slender-billed grackle Cassidix palustris	Mexico	K L
Finches and relatives: 6 forms Fringillidae	America and Africa	I

Mammals

Marsupials (35)

Southern planigale Planigale tenuirostris	New South Wales	S P
Kimberley planigale Planigale subtilissima	Northwestern Australia	S P
Red-tailed phascogale Phascogale calura	Southwestern Australia	S P
Long-tailed sminthopsis Sminthopsis longicaudata	Western Australia	S P
Eastern jerboa marsupial Antechinomys laniger	Northwestern Victoria	S P
Eastern native cat Dasyurus viverrinus	Tasmania and Victoria	B
Marsupial anteater Myrmecobius fasciatus rufus	Southwestern Australia	M
Bilby Thylacomys lagotis	Australia	H N
Lesser bilby Thylacomys leucurus	Central Australia	B D S
Pig-footed bandicoot Chaeropus ecaudatus	Australia	M S
Western ringtail Pseudocheirus occidentalis	Southwestern Australia	N
Leadbeater's opossum Gymnobelideus leadbeateri	Victoria	P I
Flinders Island wombat Phascolomys ursinus ursinus	Flinders Island	I A B
Koala Phascolarctos cinereus	Australia	I B
Brush-tailed rat-kangaroo Bettongia penicillata penicillata	Queensland	S H
Lesueur's rat-kangaroo Bettongia lesueuri	Australia	N S

Rufous rat-kangaroo Aepyprymnus rufescens	New South Wales and Queensland	H S
Desert rat-kangaroo Caloprymnus campestris	Southern Australia	A L S
Potoroo Potorous tridactylus tridactylus	Victoria	S
Banded hare-wallaby Lagostrophus fasciatus	Bernier and Dorre Islands	I O P
Rufous hare-wallaby Lagorchestes hirsutus hirsutus	Southern Australia	A
Bar-tailed rock-wallaby Petrogale xanthopus xanthopus	Southern Australia	B
Brush-tailed rock-wallaby Petrogale penicillata penicillata	Victoria and Queensland	A B
Bridled nail-tailed wallaby Onychogalea fraenata	Central Queensland	M N S
Crescent nail-tailed wallaby Onychogalea lunata	Victoria	M S
Parma wallaby Protemnodon parma	New South Wales	B I

Insectivores (4)

Haitian solenodon Solenodon paradoxus	Dominican Republic	I
Cuban solenodon Solenodon cubanus	Eastern Cuba	I

Lemurs and relatives (23)

Aye-aye Daubentonia madagascariensis	Madagascar	I
Coquerel's dwarf lemur Microcebus coquereli	Madagascar	I
Sifaka: 5 forms Propithecus verreauxi	Madagascar	I
Indris Indri indri	Madagascar	I

Monkeys and apes (7)

White-bearded spider monkey Ateles geoffroyi frontatus	Costa Rica and Nicaragua	I
Zanzibar red colobus Colobus badius kirkii	Zanzibar	B I 200
Orang-utan Pongo pygmaeus	Sumatra and Borneo	F 5000

Pygmy chimpanzee Pan paniscus	Southern Congo	I
Mountain gorilla Gorilla gorilla beringei	Eastern Congo	L 5000

Rodents (8)

Chinchilla Chinchilla lanigera	Chile	B
Kaibab squirrel Sciurus kaibabensis	Arizona	I
Utah prairie dog Cynomys parvidens	Utah	L
European beaver Castor fiber	Europe	L A B G

Sea cows (4)

Dugong Dugong dugong	Indian Ocean	A
West Indian manatee Trichechus manatus	Caribbean Sea	A
West African manatee Trichechus senegalensis	Senegalese coast	A

Whales (8)

Pacific right whale Eubalaena sieboldi	North Pacific	A
Atlantic right whale Eubalaena glacialis	North Atlantic	A
Southern right whale Eubalaena australis	Southern seas	A
Bowhead Balaena mysticetus	North Atlantic	A
Humpback whale Megaptera novaeanglia	Southern seas	A
Blue whale Balaenoptera musculus	Southern seas	A 500–2000
Fin whale Balaenoptera physalus	world wide	A 40,000
Pacific gray whale Eschrichtius gibbosus	Pacific Ocean	A 5000

Carnivores (16)

Indian cheetah Acinonyx jubatus venaticus	India	B L
African cheetah Acinonyx jubatus jubatus	Africa	B L

Bali tiger Panthera tigris balica	Bali	H L 3–4
Caspian tiger Panthera tigris virgata	Northern Iran and Turkestan	H I
Chinese Turkestan tiger Panthera tigris lecoqui	Chinese Turkestan	H L
Korean tiger Panthera tigris coreensis	Korea, Mongolia, Manchuria	H
Manchurian tiger Panthera tigris longipilis	Amur and Ussuri regions of Siberia	H G B
Indian lion Panthera leo persica	Gir forest (Northwest India)	D L 250
Barbary lynx Lynx caracal algira	Northwest Africa	H
Spanish lynx Felis lynx pardina	Sierra Morena in southern Spain	H 200
Fossa Cryptoprocta ferox	Madagascar	I
Fossane Fossa fossa	Madagascar	I
Black-footed ferret Mustela nigripes	Dakota, Montana (U.S.A.)	H
Giant panda Ailuropoda melanoleuca	Szechuan, China	

Seals and walruses (12)

Hawaiian monk seal Monachus schauinslandi	Hawaiian Islands	B 1500
Caribbean monk seal Monachus tropicalis	Jamaica	B 50
Mediterranean monk seal Monachus monachus	Mediterranean and Black Seas	B 1000– 5000
Northern elephant seal Mirounga angustirostris	California	B 8000– 10,000
Eastern harbour seal Phoca vitulina mellonae	Seal Lakes in Labrador	B 500
Atlantic walrus Odobenus rosmarus rosmarus	North Atlantic	C B 20,000– 40,000
Pacific walrus Odobenus rosmarus divergens	North Pacific	C 20,000
Guadalupe fur seal Arctocephalus philippi townsendi	Guadalupe	B 200–500
Philippi's fur seal Arctocephalus philippi philippi	Juan Fernandez	B 50

Galapagos fur seal Arctocephalus australis galapagoensis	Galapagos	B 500
Japanese sea lion Zalophus californianus japonicus	Japan	B

Elephants (2)

Ceylon elephant Elephas maximus ceylanicus	Ceylon	A I 1000
Sumatra elephant Elephas maximus sumatranus	Sumatra	A 100

Aardvarks (1)

Eriksson's aardvark Orycteropus afer erikssoni	Ituri Forest in the Congo	A

Horses and relatives (14)
(*Perissodactyla*)

Black rhinoceros Diceros bicornis	East Africa	G 13,000
Square-lipped rhinoceros Diceros simus	Sudan and Congo	G C 3900
Sumatran rhinoceros Didermoceros sumatrensis	Burma, Malaya, Sumatra	G 150
Javan rhinoceros Rhinoceros sondaicus	Java	G 25
Great Indian rhinoceros Rhinoceros unicornis	India and Nepal	G 600
Baird's tapir Tapirus bairdii	Panama, Costa Rica, Mexico	A I
Przewalski's wild horse Equus przewalski	Mongolia	A
Cape mountain zebra Equus zebra zebra	Cape Province in South Africa	A 81
Indian wild ass Equus hemionus khur	Northwest India	V A 870
Persian wild ass Equus hemionus onager	Northeastern Iran, Northwest Afghanistan	A 300
Mongolian wild ass Equus hemionus hemionus	Central Mongolia	A
Somali wild ass Equus asinus somalicus	Somalia and Ethiopia	A 1400
Nubian wild ass Equus asinus africanus	Sudan	A 300

Cattle and relatives (72)
(*Artiodactyla*)

Wild sheep: 3 forms Ovis musimon	Asia and Cyprus	A
Markhor Capra falconeri	Turkestan and Pakistan	A
Walia ibex Capra walie	Ethiopia	A C 150
Nubian ibex Capra ibex nubiana	Egypt, Sudan, Israel, Jordan	A 3000
Cretan wild goat Capra hircus cretica	Crete	A 100
Nilgiri tahr Hemitragus hylocrius	South India	A C 800
Arabian tahr Hemitragus jayakari	Oman	A
Takin: 2 forms Budorcas taxicolor	Burma and India	A
Japanese serow Capricornis crispus crispus	Japan	A I 1500
Sumatran serow Capricornis sumatrensis sumatrensis	Sumatra	A
Cuvier's gazelle Gazella gazella cuvieri	Atlas Mountains	A 600
Slender-horned gazelle: 2 forms Gazella leptoceros	Sahara	A
Mhorr Gazella dama mhorr	Southwest Morocco	G
Dibatag Ammodorcas clarkei	Somalia	A 1500
Zanzibar suni Nesotragus moschatus moschatus	Zanzibar	A
White-tailed gnu Connochaetes gnu	South Africa	A B H 600
Swayne's hartebeest Alcelaphus buselaphus swaynei	Ethiopia	A V
Hunter's hartebeest Damaliscus hunteri	Somalia and Kenya	
Bontebok Damaliscus dorcas dorcas	South Africa	A H 600
Addax Addax nasomaculatus	Southern Sahara	A
Arabian oryx Oryx leucoryx	Arabia	D 200

Giant sable antelope Hippotragus niger variani	Angola	A 500
Wild yak Bos grunniens mutus	Central Tibet	A
Kouprey Bos sauveli	Northern Cambodia	I 800
Eastern asiatic wild ox Bibos javanicus	Java, Borneo, Burma, Thailand	A I
Malayan gaur Bos gaurus hubacki	Malay Peninsula	A C I 300
Tamarau Anoa mindorensis	Mindoro	I A
Anoa: 3 forms Anoa depressicornis	Celebes	A I
Wild Indian buffalo Bubalus bubalis	Assam, Nepal and India	A V 2100
Wisent Bison bonasus bonasus	Poland and U.S.S.R.	I 500
Western giant eland Taurotragus derbianus derbianus	Guinea and Ivory Coast	A V 50–100
Reindeer and Caribou: 3 forms Rangifer tarandus	Lappland and North America	A D
Red deer and wapiti: 6 forms Cervus elaphus	Asia and North Africa	A G
Père David's deer Elaphurus davidianus	only in zoos	390
Sika deer: 6 forms Cervus nippon	Japan and East Asia	A G I
Brow-antlered deer: 3 forms Cervus eldi	Burma and Thailand	A
Bawean deer Hyelaphus kuhlii	Bawean Island (north of Java)	A I
Florida key deer Odocoileus virginianus clavium	Florida Keys	A I 235
Mesopotamian fallow deer Dama mesopotamica	Southwest Iran	A I 50–60
Wild bactrian camel Camelus bactrianus ferus	Gobi–Trans Altai desert	A 400
Pygmy hog Porcula salvania	Nepal, Sikkim and Assam	L

Literature

Detailed bibliographies can be found in the following books:

Allen, G. M.: Extinct and Vanishing Mammals of the Western Hemisphere. Spec. Publ. Am. Comm. Internat. Wild Life Protection, Nr. 11, New York 1942.
Greenway, J. C.: Extinct and Vanishing Birds of the World. Spec. Publ. Am. Comm. Internat. Wild Life Protection, Nr. 13, New York 1958.
Harper, Ph.: Extinct and Vanishing Mammals of the Old World. Spec. Publ. Am. Comm. Internat. Wild Life Protection, Nr. 12, New York 1945.
IUCN: Derniers refuges, Atlas des Réserves Naturelles dans le monde. Elsevier, Bruxelles 1956.
Street, Ph.: Vanishing Animals. Faber and Faber, London 1961.

Periodicals

IUCN-Bulletin, International Union for Conservation of Nature and Natural Resources, Morges, Switzerland.
Natur und Landschaft, Bundesanstalt für Vegetationskunde, Naturschutz und Landschaftspflege, Bad Godesberg.
Oryx, The Journal of the Fauna Preservation Society, London.
Schweizer Naturschutz, Basel.
Unesco-Kurier, Paris.

Index

(**Boldface** numbers refer to Figures)